DIGITAL TECHNIQUES

DIGITAL TECHNIQUES

K. J. Bohlman
I.Eng., F.I.E.I.E.

Dickson Price Publishers Ltd
Hawthorn House
Bowdell Lane
Brookland, Kent TN29 9RW

Dickson Price Publishers Ltd
Hawthorn House
Bowdell Lane
Brookland
Kent TN29 9RW

First Published 1989
Second edition 1992
© K. J. Bohlman 1989

British Library Cataloguing in Publication Data

Bohlman, K. J. (Kenneth John)
    Digital Techniques. – 2 Rev. ed.
    I. Title
    621.3815

ISBN 0-85380-167-3

Photoset by
R. H. Services, Welwyn, Hertfordshire
Printed and bound in Great Britain by
Billing and Sons Ltd, Worcester

CONTENTS

Other Books of Interest

ELECTRONICS SERVICING VOL 1
ELECTRONICS SERVICING VOL 2
ELECTRONICS SERVICING VOL 3
ELECTRONICS SERVICING 500 MULTIPLE CHOICE QUESTIONS
    AND ANSWERS FOR PART 1
ELECTRONICS SERVICING 500 QUESTIONS AND ANSWERS FOR
    PART 2
COLOUR AND MONO TELEVISION VOL 1
COLOUR AND MONO TELEVISION VOL 2
COLOUR AND MONO TELEVISION VOL 3
PRINCIPLES OF DOMESTIC VIDEO RECORDING AND PLAYBACK
    SYSTEMS
CLOSED CIRCUIT TELEVISION VOL 1
CLOSED CIRCUIT TELEVISION VOL 2
RADIO SERVICING VOL 1
RADIO SERVICING VOL 2
RADIO SERVICING VOL 3
CONTROL SYSTEMS TECHNOLOGY
FAULT LOCATION IN ELECTRONIC EQUIPMENT
VIDEO RECORDING & PLAYBACK SYSTEMS 500 QUESTIONS AND
    ANSWERS

Inspection Copies

Lecturers wishing to examine any of these books should write to the publishers requesting an inspection copy.

Complete Catalogue available on request.

PREFACE

This book covers the **Digital Techniques** syllabus for the Part 3 of the City & Guilds 224 course in Electronics Servicing. Amongst the topics considered are **I.C. Logic Families**, **A-D Conversion**, **D-A Conversion**, **MSI Circuits**, **Interfacing** and **Visual Display Units**.

In this second edition, new material on **Binary Adders**, **Karnaugh Mapping** and the **Design of Synchronous Counters** has been added and corrections to the popular first edition carried out. The new material has been included to satisfy the needs of students following B.T.E.C. Certificate and Higher Certificate programmes offering units in Digital Electronics.

Apart from City & Guilds and B.T.E.C. students, the text will be found useful by others wishing to acquire an understanding of **semiconductor memories**, **display devices**, **data acquisition**, **signal sampling**, **keyboard encoders**, **stepper motors**, **shaft encoders** and **visual display terminals** together with practical applications.

Ken Bohlman is a Senior Lecturer in Communication Engineering at North Lincolnshire College where for over 30 years he has specialised in the teaching of Colour Television, Information Technology and Communication Radio to technicians in HNC/HND and City & Guilds 224 courses.

I.C. LOGIC FAMILIES

EARLY PRACTICAL VERSIONS of the electronic logic gate functions of AND, OR, NOT, NAND, and NOR *etc* were based on discrete component circuits using resistors, diodes and transistors. These discrete component circuits, *e.g.* diode-resistor logic (d.r.l.) and resistor-transisor logic (r.t.l.), were expensive compared with modern integrated logic families, and being inferior in performance are now rarely used.

The main reasons for the growth of digital integrated circuits (and linear i.cs.) are that they are more reliable, smaller and lighter than discrete circuits, they require fewer circuit connections and can be mass produced making them cheaper. Also, complex digital circuits can be fabricated in i.c. form that would be uneconomical using alternative techniques. Integrated circuits used for logic circuit families may be broadly divided into those based on **bipolar transistor** circuit techniques or those employing **metal oxide semiconductor devices** and both types will be considered in this chapter. Integrated circuits are often classified according to the number of components that may be accommodated on the sillicon chip as follows:

Small Scale Integration (S.S.I.) – Less than 100 components
Medium Scale Integration (M.S.I.) – 100 to 1000 components
Large Scale Integration (L.S.I.) – 1000 to 10000 components
Very Large Scale Integration (V.L.S.I.) – 10000 or more components

The choice of a logic family for a particular application is generally determined by considering its performance with respect to a number of fundamental circuit characteristics which will be considered first.

LOGIC CIRCUIT CHARACTERISTICS

Switching Speed (Propagation Delay)

In technical data, the speed of a gate is defined by its **propagation delay** and is the time taken for the output of a gate to respond to an applied input signal. The switching characteristics are asymmetrical, see Fig. 1.1 which refers to a NOT or inverter gate. The propagation delay for an input transistion from LOW to HIGH differs to that for an input transition from HIGH to LOW.

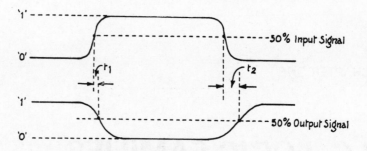

Fig. 1.1 Propagation delay.

Most manufacturers quote both of these times in their specifications and the following symbols are generally employed:

t_pLH propagation time LOW-to-HIGH level output
t_pHL propagation time HIGH-to-LOW level output

When a single propagation time is quoted this is often the average of the two times, *e.g.* in Fig.1.1 the average propagation time is

$$t_p = \frac{t_1 + t_2}{2}$$

As indicated, propagation delays are usually specified at the 50% voltage levels of input and output signals.

The propagation delay of a logic gate depends upon a number of factors including switching device characteristics, circuit design and supply voltage. One of the contributing factors for the propagation delay is charge storage in the switching device (p-n diode or transistor). This may be explained by considering a p-n diode in which the applied voltage is suddenly changed from forward to reverse bias, see Fig. 1.2(a). The forward current of the diode, see Fig. 1.2(b), does not fall immediately to zero (or its leakage value) but instead reverses. This is due to the presence of a large number of **minority** carriers on both sides of the p-n junction which have been supplied from the opposite side of the junction. These minority carriers must first be swept back across the juction to recombine with parent atoms. This occurs during the period t_1–t_2 (minority charge **storage time**) when the junction continues to conduct easily but in the reverse direction (the current being limited by external resistance in the diode circuit). It is not until t_2 when the minority carrier density has reached an equilibrium state that the **juction** voltage begins to reverse and cause the diode current to decrease. During the interval from t_2 to when the current reaches its leakage value (t_3) the juction capacitance charges via external resistance to the reverse voltage (transistion time). There is, therfore, a period of time (t_1–t_3) that is necessary for the p-n junction to 'recover' on being switched from the forward to reverse bias state, this interval represents the propagation delay.

Stray capacitance at the gate output also has a considerable effect and

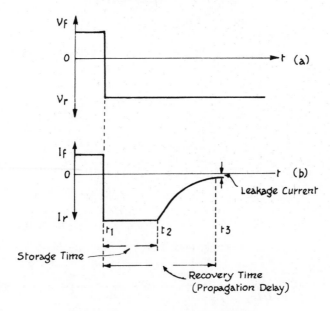

Fig. 1.2 Charge storage in p.n. junction.

figures quoted for propagation delay generally refer to a given load resistance and load capacitance which lies typically between 15 and 30pF. Most i.c. logic families have propagation delays between about 1 and 100ns.

Noise Margin

Spurious noise voltages that are of sufficiently large amplitude at the input of a logic gate may cause the logic state at the gate output to change. Such false operation of a gate will lead to errors in the performance of a logic system. The **noise margin** or **noise immunity** of a logic gate is the maximum noise voltage that can be present at the gate input without producing a change in the gate output state. Integrated circuit manufacturers usually quote d.c. values of noise margin which are defined in terms of the gate transfer characteristic, see Fig. 1.3.

For the inverter gate characteristic shown, the HIGH output voltage (logic 1) is 3V and the LOW output voltage (logic 0) is 0·2V. The point **A** on the characteristic corresponds to the gate operation when the input is at the LOW level (0·2V) and point **B** to the operating state when the input is at a HIGH level (3V). It will be noted that a logic 1 is obtained at the gate output for input voltages from 0V up to 0·9V and a logic 0 is produced at the output for input voltages from 1·1V to 3V. The transition from one logic level to the other occurs between input voltages of 0·9V and 1·1V, *i.e.* at about 1V in this case, the level of which is often referred to as the **threshold value**.

If the minimum logic 0 level at the input of the gate is taken to be 0·2V,

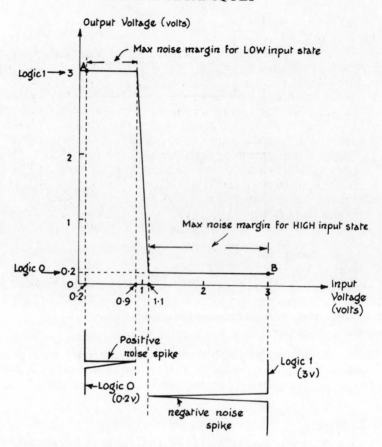

Fig. 1.3 Transfer characteristics of an inverter gate showing noise margins

then as shown a positive-going noise spike of amplitude $(0.9 - 0.2) = 0.7V$ can be superimposed on the logic 0 level without causing the logic state at the gate output to alter. This represents the maximum or best noise margin for the low input state. Should the allowable maximum logic 0 voltage at the gate input be $0.4V$ then the noise margin would be reduced to $(0.9 - 0.4) = 0.5V$ (call this the worst case).

Similarly, if the maximum logic 1 level at the gate input is 3V, then a negative-going noise spike of amplitude $(3 - 1.1) = 1.9V$ can be superimposed on the logic 1 input level as shown without causing the output state of the gate to change. This represents the maximum or best noise margin for the high input state. A reduction in the logic 1 level at the gate input to, say, 2V would reduce the noise margin to $(2 - 1.1) = 0.9V$ (call this the other worst case). Usually the smaller of the two worst cases is quoted for the noise margin which for the examples considered would be $0.5V$.

Power Dissipation

It is necessary to know the power dissipation of a gate in order to determine the power supply requirements of a logic system and assumes particular importance in choosing suitable logic devices for systems operating from batteries. Most logic gates demand a different current from the supply depending upon whether the output is HIGH or LOW. Typical values quoted are often the average of the two current values, although many manufacturers quote i.c. supply currents for all outputs LOW and for all outputs HIGH (note that most i.cs. have several gates on one silicon slice).

Logic i.c. families usually operate with a d.c. supply of about 5V and the d.c. power dissipation per gate ranges typically from about 10μW to 100mW depending upon the logic family. Although the power dissipation per gate is quite small, if a system consists of many thousands of logic gates the total power may be quite appreciable and the heat produced will need to be got rid of using suitable ventilation or perhaps cooling fans.

Operating Temperature Range

A logic device will only operate satisfactorily and meet its specification if its working (ambient) temperature is kept within a specified range. Two standard ambient temperature ranges are widely used:

Military standard $-55°$C to $+125°$C
Industrial standard $0°$C to $+70°$C

Some logic families are available to meet both specifications but others are available in only restricted temperature ranges.

Fan-in and Fan-out

The **fan-in** of a logic gate is the maximum number of separate inputs which may be applied to the gate without affecting its performance. In many cases fan-in is determined by the switching speed of the gate, since one limit on the switching speed is the total stray capacitance added by the separate inputs to the gate.

The **fan-out** of a logic gate is the maximum number of gate inputs that the gate may supply simultaneously without causing the output logic level to fall outside its specification. It is assumed here that the gate inputs belong to the same family as the gate output that is supplying them. This gate characteristic is considered again later in the chapter.

LOGIC FAMILIES

Transistor-Transistor Logic (TTL)

TTL i.c. logic gates are based on bipolar transistor technology and the diagram of Fig. 1.4 shows the equivalent circuit of a single TTL NAND gate. TR1 is a multi-emitter transistor which effectively produces the AND

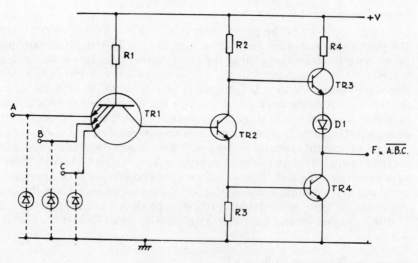

Fig. 1.4 TTL NAND gate.

function. TR2 is a phase splitting amplifier and produces complementary logic signals at its collector and emitter. These signals drive TR3 and TR4 which form the output stage, often referred to as a 'totem-pole' output due to its circuit shape. TR3 and TR4 provide active drive with either a LOW or HIGH output state and allow capacitive loads to be readily driven. TR3 may be regarded as the active load for TR4 and the two transistors are sometimes referred to as the active 'pull-up' and 'pull-down' transistors respectively.

If the logic inputs A, B and C and all HIGH, say, +5V then the effective circuit for TR1 and TR2 is as shown in Fig. 1.5(a) with TR1 collector-base junction acting as a diode supplying the base current to TR2 which is 'on' and saturated. As a result TR2 collector is LOW and its emitter is HIGH, causing TR3 to turn 'off' and for TR4 to turn 'on'. Thus the output at F will be LOW.

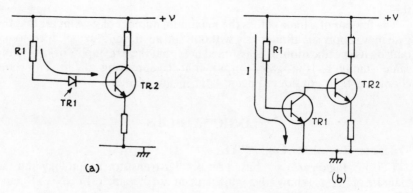

Fig. 1.5 Circuits showing the action of TR1 for different logic inputs.

With any or all of the logic inputs at LOW level, say, 0V then the effective circuit for TR1 is as illustrated in Fig. 1.5(b). The current that was in TR2 base is diverted through TR1 base emitter junction thus TR1 is 'on' and TR2 is 'off'. In consequence TR2 collector is HIGH and its emitter is LOW causing TR3 to turn 'on' and for TR4 to turn 'off'. The output at F will then be HIGH.

Under the condition of all logic inputs in the HIGH state, TR4 is 'on' and to ensure that TR3 is held 'off', the diode D1 is included. The potentials pertaining then are: TR4 base 0·7V, TR3 base 0·9V and TR4 collector 0·2V. The 0·7V existing between TR3 base and TR4 collector would (without D1) probably cause TR3 to turn on. However with D1 in circuit the 0·7V is shared between D1 and TR3 base-emitter ensuring that TR3 remains 'off'.

When the output at F changes logic state, TR3 and TR4 may conduct simultaneously for a brief period resulting in a current surge through the output pair. To limit the current surge, the resistor R4 is included. The diodes (shown dotted) connected at the gate inputs are normally incorporated in all TTL gates, although not always shown in diagrams. These act as clamp diodes to reduce the effect of negative overswing on logic pulses due to inductive effects in interconnections between TTL elements.

Sinking and Sourcing

When the output of one TTL gate drives the input of another TTL gate, the driving gate either supplies current to the driven gate, this is called **sourcing**, or the driving gate takes current from the driven gate, this is called **sinking**. It is conventional to treat current entering a gate terminal as being positive; hence currents which leave the gate connection are taken to be negative. In manufacturers data therfore, 'sink' currents are given positive sign whilst 'source' currents are given negative sign.

With the output of the driving gate in the LOW state as in Fig. 1.6, the

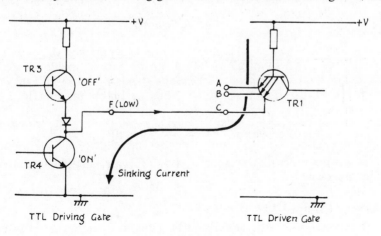

Fig. 1.6 Sinking.

driving gate is said to sink current, *i.e.* provide a current path to the zero volt rail. For a standard 74/54 TTL gate the maximum output current with the output in the LOW state (I_{OL}) is typically 16mA, *i.e.* the gate is capable of sinking 16mA. The maximum input current of a standard 74/54 TTL gate with the input at the LOW level (I_{IL}) is typically $-1\cdot6$mA (note the minus sign). Using this data the maximum fan-out for the standard 74/54 TTL gate may be established for the LOW output state:

$$\text{Fan-out} = \frac{I_{OL}}{I_{IL}} = \frac{16 \text{ mA}}{1\cdot6 \text{ mA}} = 10$$

The diagram of Fig. 1.7 shows the situation when the output of the driving gate is in the HIGH state. This time the driving gate has to source, *i.e.* supply current to the driven gate.

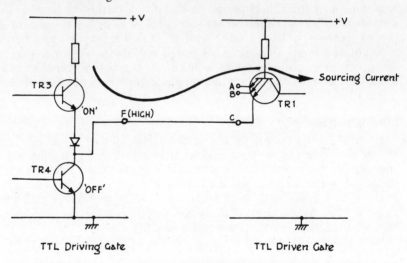

Fig. 1.7 Sourcing.

For a standard 74/54 TTL gate the output current with the output in the HIGH state (I_{OH}) is typically -400μA, *i.e.* the gate is capable of supplying a current of 400μA. The input current of a standard 74/54 TTL gate with the input HIGH (I_{IH}) is typically 40μA. Thus the fan-out for the HIGH output state is:

$$\text{Fan-out} = \frac{I_{OH}}{I_{IH}} = \frac{400 \text{ } \mu A}{40 \text{ } \mu A} = 10$$

It follows therefore that a standard 74/54 TTL gate can drive up to ten gates simultaneously.

Schottky Clamped TTL (STTL)

The transistors used in standard TTL gates are operated in the 'saturated' mode, *i.e.* when switched 'on' the collector current attains its maximum possible value and the collector-emitter voltage falls to a very low value. The diagram of Fig. 1.8 shows the output characteristics of a common emitter transistor operated with a load R_L from a supply V_{CC}.

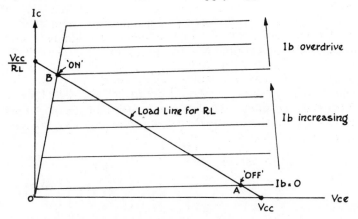

Fig. 1.8 Transistor as a switch.

With $I_b = 0$, point **A** on the load line corresponds to the 'off' condition of the transistor. If the base current is progressively raised from zero the operating point will progressively move from point **A** to the 'on' region at point **B**. If the base current is further increased beyond the value to reach point **B** using base current 'overdrive', it is found that although the emitter current will rise the collector current remains constant (saturated) and the collector-base junction becomes **forward** biassed. When the collector-base junction becomes forward biassed, the transistor is said to be saturated or 'bottomed' and Vce falls to a very low value, typically 100mV. By operating a transistor in the saturated mode, the **turn on** time of a transistor may be reduced, see Fig. 1.9. As the base drive current is increased to two or three

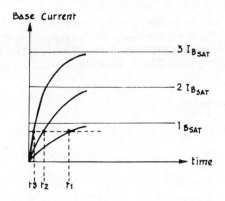

Fig. 1.9 Reducing the turn-on time of a transistor using base current overdrive.

times the saturation value, the turn-on time is progressively reduced from t_1 to t_3 as shown.

Base current overdrive, although reducing turn-on time has the disadvantage of increasing the turn-off time since it tends to increase the storage time or charge storage (see page 2). Efforts to reduce the storage time of bipolar devices led to the use of the Schottky diode, see Fig. 1.10. This diode has a junction that is formed between a metal (aluminium) and N-type semiconductor. The conduction in the device does not depend upon minority carriers in any way (only majority carriers). This virtually eleminates charge storage and reduces turn-off time. The I/V characteristic is similar to an ordinary p-n diode except that the 'cut-in' voltage is about 0·4V as opposed to about 0·7V for an ordinary p-n diode.

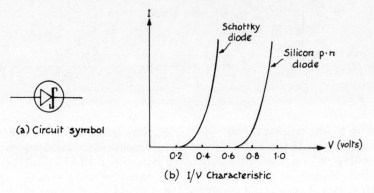

(a) Circuit symbol

(b) I/V Characteristic

Fig. 1.10 Schottky diode.

To achieve a fast turn-off time with transistors, a Schottky diode is used which is effectively connected between collector and base, see Fig. 1.11(b). Here the Schottky diode is employed as a clamp between collector and base which prevents the transistor entering into full saturation. As the transistor commences to enter into saturation conditions by increasing the base drive current, the Schottky diode clamps the voltage across the collector-base junction to 0·4V which is less than the voltage required to turn the collector-base junction into the fully forward conducting condition of say 0·7V.

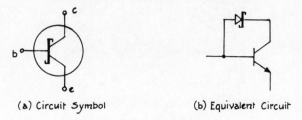

(a) Circuit Symbol

(b) Equivalent Circuit

Fig. 1.11 Schottky transistor.

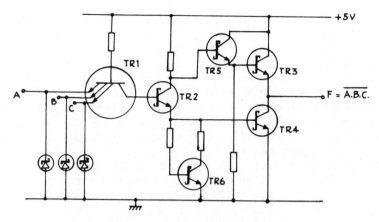

Fig. 1.12 Schottky TTL NAND gate.

A circuit diagram for a Schottky TTL NAND gate is given in Fig. 1.12. It will be seen that this is very similar to the standard TTL NAND gate of Fig. 1.4. One of the differences is the use of a Darlington pair TR5/TR3 in place of TR3 and the hold-off diode D1 which gives a better transient response. Another improvement is the inclusion of TR6 from TR2 emitter and TR4 base. This has the effect of sharpening the transition between the output states and provides a faster switching action.

Low Power Schottky TTL (LSTTL)

When a transistor is operated in either the 'on' or 'off' condition, see Fig. 1.13, the power dissipated in the device is small. In the 'off' state the V_{CE} of the transistor is practically equal to V_{CC} but the collector current is

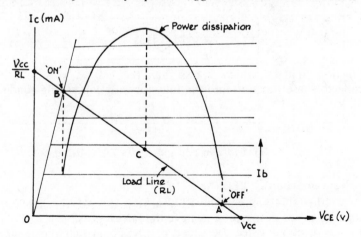

Fig. 1.13 Relationship between operating point and collector power dissipation.

very small and is due to the leakage current I_{CEO} which with a modern transistor is only a few μA. As a result the collector power dissipation is low. In the 'on' state, although the collector current is large, the V_{CE} is small, say, 0·2V and again the collector power dissipation is low.

In switching, however, between the 'on' and 'off' states the collector dissipation rises, as shown as the operating point moves along the load line, reaching a maximum when the operating point correponds to point C. The mean power dissipated in a transistor, and hence in a TTL gate, also depends upon the **transition speed** between states and the frequency at which the switching takes place.

In designing low power gates, a number of factors have to be considered including transistion speed, dissipation in the 'on' state, circuit capacitances and choice of devices used. Low Power Schottky TTL is an example of modern i.c. bipolar gate technology which is now the preferred system for TTL and is used extensively in MSI, LSI and VLSI form. An example of a Low Power Schottky TTL NAND gate is given in Fig. 1.14, but circuits differ in detail from one manufacturer to another. Here the multi-emitter transistor is eliminated and is replaced by Schottky diodes (D1 and D2). With inputs A and B both HIGH (+5V), D1 and D2 are 'off', thus TR1 is 'on' causing TR5 to be 'on' and TR4 to be 'off'. The output at F is therefore LOW. D3 and D4 are speed-up diodes to discharge circuit capacitances.

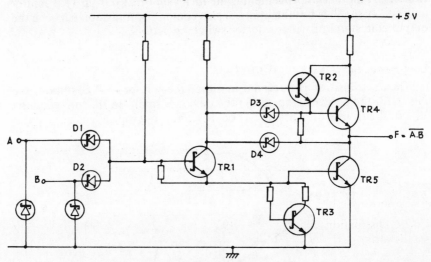

Fig. 1.14 Low power Schottky TTL NAND gate.

Advanced Schottky TTL (ASTTL)

Another sub-family of the TTL range is the Advanced Schottky. These logic gates are designed to achieve the fastest possible speed of operation; they give about twice the speed of LSTTL at half the input power. A respresentative circuit is shown in Fig. 1.15 which is similar to that of

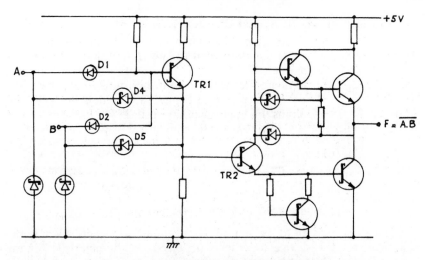

Fig. 1.15 Advanced Schottky TTL NAND gate.

Fig. 1.14. The main changes are the addition of two more speed-up diodes (D3 and D4) to discharge TR2 base capacitance and the inclusion of an emitter-follower TR1 which gives further current gain. Additionally, the input diodes (D1 and D2) have been replaced by conventional p-n diodes which give a better noise immunity than Schottky diodes. Advanced Schottky TTL gates are featured in V.L.S.I. systems.

A comparison of some of the parameters for the TTL sub-families are given in Table 1.1.

	Standard TTL 54/74	Schottky TTL 54S/74S	Low Power Schottky TTL 54LS/74LS	Advanced Schottky TTL 54AS/74AS
Propagation Delay (nano-seconds)	10	3	10	1·5
Power Dissipation (milli-watts)	10	19	2	1
Fan-out	10	10	10	10
Noise Immunity (volts)	0·4	0·3	0·3	0·55
Toggle Speed (max) (MHz)	15	125	25	200

Table 1.1 Comparison of TTL Sub-families

Pin-Out Diagrams and Electrical Characteristics

Logic integrated circuits are produced in a number of different packages. The most common is the standard dual in-line (DIL) plastic or ceramic package but flat packages are also available, see Fig. 1.16. The pin numbers of the package are numbered as viewed from the top of the device, see Fig. 1.17. Standard DIL plastic packages are available with either 8, 14, 16, 18, 20, 22, 24, 28 or 40 pins. Flat packages have usually 10, 14, 12 or 24 pins but the pin numbers are different to the standard DIL packages.

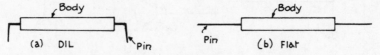

Fig. 1.16 End views of dual-in-line and flat packages.

Information relating to the pin-out connections are usually given in the data sheet for the device together with electrical characteristics of the device. Typical electrical parameters for a Schottky TTL 2-Input NAND gate are given below:

Parameter

Max. supply voltage Vcc	7V
Max. input voltage V_{IN}	5·5V
Operating free-air temperature T_A	
Series 54	−55C to 125C (Military)
Series 74	0C to 70C (Commercial)
Input Voltage	
Low level, V_{IL}	0·8V (max)
High level, V_{IH}	2·0V (min)
Output Voltage	
Low level, V_{OL}	0·4V (max) - typically 0·22V
High level, V_{OH}	2·4 (min) - typically 3·3V
Input Current	
Low level, I_{IL}	−1·6mA (max)
High level, I_{IH}	40μA (max)
Output Current	
Low level, I_{OL}	−16mA (max)
High level, I_{OH}	−400μA (max)
Propagation Delay Time	
Low-to-High, t_{PLH}	4·5ns (max) - typically 3ns
High-to-Low, t_{PHL}	5ns (max) - typically 3ns
	(C_L = 15pF, R_L = 280ohm)

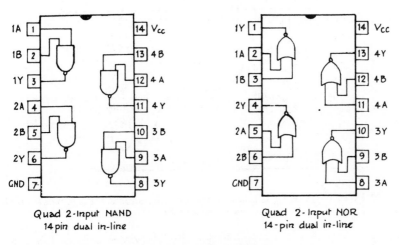

Fig. 1.17 Pin-out diagrams.

Wired Logic

It is a great asset in designing combinational logic systems to be able to connect the outputs of individual logic gates together. This feature is called **wired** or **collector** logic. The example given in Fig. 1.18 shows the outputs of two NAND gates connected together. This connection, assuming positive logic, is called **wired-AND** because if F1 = 1 and F2 = 1, then F = 1, whereas if F1 = 0 and/or F2 = 0, then F = 0. TTL gates with totem pole outputs are not suitable for such a connection, see Fig. 1.19. If the output of gate A is wired to the output of gate B, then if the output of gate A happens to be HIGH when the output of gate B is LOW or vice-versa excessive power will be developed in the 'on' transistors possibly resulting in damage to both gates.

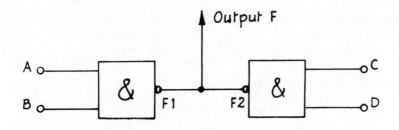

Fig. 1.18 Wired-logic.

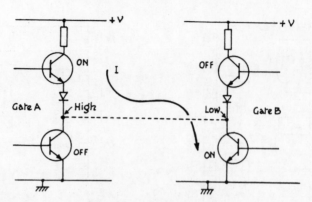

Fig. 1.19 *Excessive power dissipation in the 'on' transistors if TTL totem pole outputs are wired together.*

Open-Collector Output

One solution to the limitation of wiring the outputs of TTL gates together is to use an **open-collector** output stage, see Fig. 1.20. Here the totem pole output stage has been replaced by a single transistor TR3 with an open-circuit collector output. The output of one such gate can now be joined to the output of a similar gate, but an external 'pull-up' resistor must be connected between the common output line and the supply rail, see Fig. 1.21.

The value of the pull-up resistor R_L depends upon the number of open-collector gates that are wired together and the fan-out. The minimum value of R_L is determined by the fan-out, see Fig. 1.22(a). The maximum current I_3 flowing through either of the open-collector output transistors must not exceed 16mA, thus the minimum value of R_L is given by:

$$R_L = \frac{V_{CC} - V_{OL}}{I_3 - I_2} \text{ohms}$$

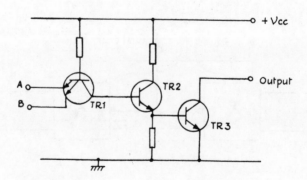

Fig. 1.20 *TTL NAND gate open-collector.*

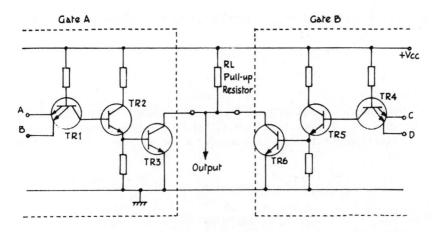

Fig. 1.21 Outputs of two TTL open-collector NAND gates connected together (wired-AND).

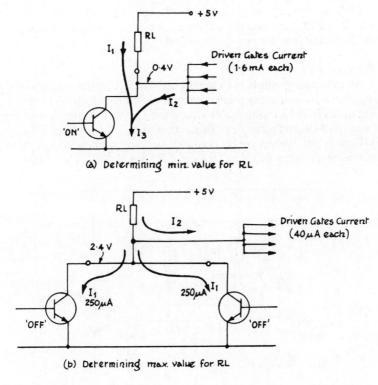

(a) Determining min. value for RL

(b) Determining max. value for RL

Fig. 1.22 Diagrams showing currents for the commoned high and low voltage output states.

With a fan-out of four then $I_2 = 6\cdot4mA$ and with $V_{CC} = 5V$ and $V_{OL} = 0\cdot4V$,

$$R_L \text{ (min)} = \frac{5 - 0\cdot4}{16 - 6.4} \text{ k-ohm}$$

$$\simeq 480 \text{ ohm}$$

The maximum value for R_L is determined from the circuit condition when the commoned output is high, see Fig. 1.22(b). The current supplied via R_L is the sum of the driven gate currents (I_2) and the leakage current I_1 for each of the commoned gates ($250\mu A$ max). Thus the maximum value for R_L is given by:

$$R_L = \frac{V_{CC} - V_{OH}}{I_2 + m\,I_1} \text{ ohms (where m is the number of commoned gates)}$$

With $V_{CC} = 5V$, $V_{OH} = 2\cdot4V$ and with 2 commoned gates,

$$R_L \text{ (max)} = \frac{5 - 2\cdot4}{0\cdot16 + 0\cdot5} \text{ k-ohm}$$

$$\simeq 3\cdot9 \text{ k-ohm}$$

The switching speed of the open-collector TTL gate is lower than that of a standard TTL gate and the advantage of the low output impedance in both the high and low output states is lost.

Tri-State TTL

An alternative solution to the problem of wiring the outputs of TTL gates together is to use a **Tri-State** device, a circuit of which is given in Fig. 1.23. When a HIGH (about $3\cdot6V$) is applied to the Inhibit/Enable input, TR6 turns hard-on and saturates. This action turns TR1 'on' and TR2 'off'. When TR2 goes 'off', the diode D1 conducts keeping the base of TR3 below cut-on potential. As a result TR3, TR4 and TR5 are all 'off'. The output at F is then

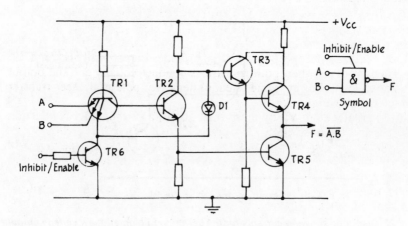

Fig. 1.23 Tri-state TTL NAND gate.

in the third or tri-state when the output imepdance is high, but the logic level is undefined. The gate is then effectively disabled.

When a LOW (about $0 \cdot 2V$) is applied to the Inhibit/Enable terminal, TR6 is 'off' and so is D1. In this mode the circuit is enabled and works normally. Thus the output at F can, depending upon the A and B inputs, assume either logic 1 or logic 0 (the other two states) with low output impedance.

A number of tri-state devices can thus be connected to a common line or data bus with only one tri-state gate being enabled at any one time. An example of three tri-state NOT buffer gates driving a common line is shown in Fig. 1.24. In response to enabling signals, the three gates are able to supply the data at their inputs one at a time to the common data bus. Tri-state TTL is virtually a mandatory requirement in micro-computer systems because of the large number of devices connected to the common bus system which may be bidirectional.

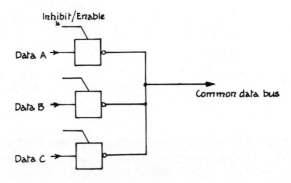

Fig. 1.24 Tri-state buffers.

Emitter Coupled Logic (ECL)

The basic building block of emitter-coupled logic is the difference (differential) amplifier, a basic circuit of which is given in Fig. 1.25(a). TR1 and TR2 have equal value collector loads and share a common emitter resistor. A fixed reference voltage (V_R) provides the forward bias for TR2. If v_i is equal to V_R then both transistors conduct equally and the output voltage v_O will be at some steady negative potential, see transfer characteristic of Fig. 1.25(b).

If v_i is greater than V_R by more than about $0 \cdot 1V$ then TR1 conduction increases and TR2 turns 'off'. Conversely if v_i is less than V_R by about $0 \cdot 1V$, TR2 conduction increases and TR1 turns 'off'. During the transition period the current in one transistor is diverted to the other so that the total current in R_E (i_3) remains essentially constant, *i.e.* the current supplied by the d.c. supply remains essentially constant. Except for a small range of input voltage when when v_i differs from V_R by less than $0 \cdot 1V$, the output voltage assumes one of two possible voltage levels or logic states.

An important feature of the circuit, decided by the chosen parameters, is

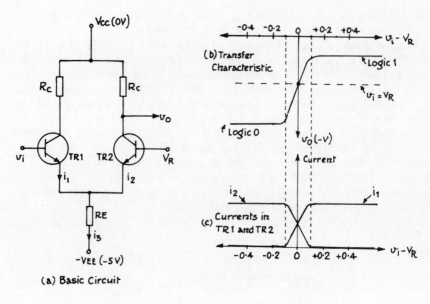

Fig. 1.25 Operation of difference amplifier.

that when a transistor is 'on' **neither TR1 nor TR2 is allowed to go into saturation**. This virtually eliminates the storage time and the ECL gate is the fastest of all the logic families; propagation delays as small as 0·5ns are possible.

ECL OR/NOR Gate

A circuit of a standard 2-input ECL OR/NOR gate is given in Fig. 1.26. The difference amplifier is formed by TR1, TR2 and TR3 with collector loads R1 and R2 and share a common emitter resistor R3. Note that the parallel connection of TR1 and TR2 form one 'leg' of the differential amplifier. A fixed reference voltage of $-1·29V$ is supplied to TR3 base from the voltage reference circuit comprising R4,D1,D2,R5 and the emitter-follower TR4. Complementary outputs are taken from the collectors of TR1/TR2 and TR3 via emitter-followers TR5 and TR6 to provide OR and NOR functions. Pull-down resistors are required for the 'open-emitter' outputs.

If inputs A and B are at logic 0 $(-1·75V)$, then both TR1 and TR2 are 'off' and TR3 is 'on'. The current in R3 is then supplied by TR3 and there is a voltage drop across R2 of $0·85V$. The output from TR5 emitter is equal to the voltage drop across R2 plus TR5 Vbe $(0·9V)$ giving an output voltage of $-1·75V$ (logic 0). Since there is no voltage drop across R1 (TR1 and TR2 'off') the output from TR6 emitter is $-0·9V$ (TR6 Vbe) which corresponds to logic 1.

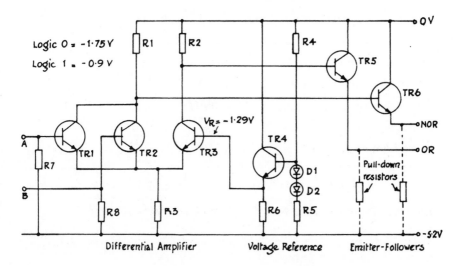

Fig. 1.26 Integrated circuit ECL OR/NOR gate.

When either inputs A or B are at logic 1 (−0·9V) then TR1 or TR2 will be 'on' and TR3 will be 'off'. Current in R3 will then be diverted from TR3 to either TR1 or TR2 and there will be a voltage drop across R1 of 0·85V. The NOR output will then be −1·75V (logic 0) and the OR output will be −0·9V (logic 1).

The high input impendance of the difference amplifier and the use of the low output impedance emitter-followers TR5 and TR6 permit a high fan-out, typically 50. When the output of one ECL gate is used to drive the input of another ECL gate, the output pull-down resistors (shown dotted) may be provided by the input pull-down resistors (R7 and R8) of the driven gate. Another advantage of R7 and R8 is that unused inputs may be left disconnected and will then be at logic 0. The main characteristics of the ECL gate are:

(a) The highest speed of any logic family is attained since the transistors do not saturate.
(b) The power dissipation is relatively high compared with other logic families.
(c) Since the current drawn from the supply is essentially constant, decoupling problems are eased and there is less interaction between i.cs. mounted on the same p.c.b.
(d) Complementary outputs are available enhancing the logic capability.
(e) High d.c. fan-out.
(f) Voltage level shifters are required for interfacing with other logic families.
(g) Since only a small voltage difference exists between the two logic states the noise margin is only about 200mV.

Typical dynamic characteristics for an ECL gate are given in Table 1.2.

Propagation Delay	2ns
Power Dissipation (per gate)	25mW
Toggle Speed	250MHz
Fan-out	>50
Noise immunity	0·2V

Table 1.2 Dynamic Characteristics of ECL gate

Electrical Parameters for 10101 Quad 2-input OR/NOR ECL gate

Logic diagram

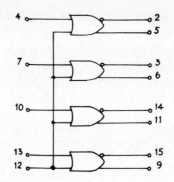

Fig. 1.27 Logic diagram 10101 quad 2-input OR/NOR ECL gate.

Parameter

Supply Current I_E	25mA (max)
Input Current	
Low level, I_{IL}	0·5μA (min)
High level, I_{IH}	265μA (max)
Input Voltage	
Low level, V_{IL}	−1·85V
High level, V_{IH}	−0·81V
Output Voltage	
Low level, V_{OL}	−1·89V min (−1·675V max)
High level, V_{OH}	−0·89V max (−1·06V min)

Metal Oxide Semiconductor (MOS)

The MOS i.c. logic family is based on the use of single channel metal oxide semiconductor transistors. Originally, P-channel (PMOS) devices were used but once N-channel (NMOS) technology was mastered it took over from PMOS. N-channel devices have the advantage of a higher electron mobility than with P-channel and hence a faster switching speed; also they provide compatibility with TTL as regards logic levels and supply voltage.

MOS devices are physically smaller than their bipolar counterparts giving a reduction in cost per gates, their input resistance is high (10^{10}ohms) and MOS devices can be used to replace resistors. A disadvantage of MOS is their relatively slower switching speed compared to bipolar devices; this is due to the input capacitance arising out of the oxide layer between the gate electrode and conducting channel.

An N-channel MOS NOR gate is given in Fig. 1.28(a) which employs enhancement mode devices. TR4 is used as an active load resistor for inverter transistors TR1,TR2 and TR3. When 1 or more of the inputs are HIGH, the appropriate inverter transistor conducts and the output is LOW. If all of the inputs are LOW, TR1–TR3 are 'off' and the output is HIGH. The equivalent NAND gate circuit is given in Fig. 1.28(b) where again TR4 is used as an active load resistor. The output is LOW only when all of the inputs are HIGH since then TR1,TR2 and TR3 will all be 'on'. For any other input combination, the output will be HIGH. Note that during only 1 of the 8 possible input conditions is power taken from the power supply to the NAND gate whereas for the NOR gate power is delivered for 7 out of the 8 possible conditions.

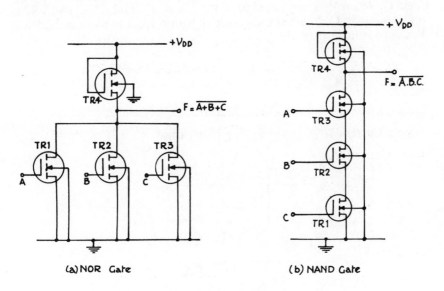

(a) NOR Gate   (b) NAND Gate

Fig. 1.28 NMOS gates.

HMOS (High Performance MOS)

For use in Very Large Scale Integrated circuits the dimensions of the MOSFET are scaled down. In a MOSFET transistor, the propagation delay is minimised by reducing the horizontal and vertical dimensions of the conducting channel and by increasing the channel doping concentration. This scaling-down of dimensions and scaling-up of doping levels to produce minature MOSFET devices is given the generic name HMOS. With a scaling-down factor of 0.4, the channel length is reduced to 2μm from 5μm giving gate delays of the order of 0.4ns.

Size reduction has been achieved through new manufacturing technologies by generally using electron and X-ray processes in place of the more traditional photographic methods.

Complementary Metal Oxide Semiconductor (CMOS)

This i.c. logic family is based on the use of a mixture of P-channel and N-channel metal oxide semiconductor transistors. CMOS devices are cheap to manufacture, have an extremely low power dissipation and a small area of fabrication. These advantages lend themselves to large scale integration such as computer memories. The noise margin is high but the propagation delay is longer than for other families.

CMOS logic is based on the inverter gate shown in Fig. 1.29. Here complementary, enhancement mode transistors are connected in series between $+V_{DD}$ and earth. When V_i is zero voltage (logic 0), TR1 is 'on' and TR2 is 'off (note that TR1 gate is then negative with respect to its source); the output voltage V_O is then practically equal to the supply rail, $+V_{DD}$ (logic 1). When V_i is, say equal to $+V_{DD}$ (logic 1), TR2 is 'on' and TR2 is 'off' (note that TR2 gate is then positive with respect to its source); V_O is then zero voltage (logic 0).

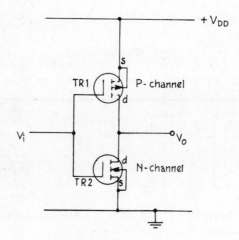

Fig. 1.29 CMOS inverter gate.

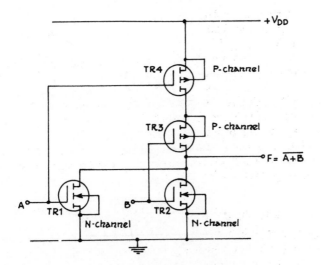

Fig. 1.30 CMOS NOR gate.

In both output logic states, the output impedance is low because either TR1 or TR2 is 'on' and saturated. CMOS provides a very low power dissipation because when a p-channel device is 'on' an n-channel device is 'off' and vice-versa and no d.c. current flows from $+V_{DD}$ to earth (it is assumed here that the output is connected to another CMOS gate which being of very high input impedance takes only a very small input current).

A CMOS NOR gate using enhancement mode transistors is given in Fig. 1.30. When inputs A and B are LOW (logic 0), the P-channel devices TR3 and TR4 are 'on' and the N-channel devices TR1 and TR2 are 'off'. The 'on' transistors are low resistance channels and the 'off' transistors are high resistance channels, resulting in the output voltage being nearly equal to the supply voltage which is logic 1. When either A or B, or both, are HIGH (logic 1), TR1 or TR2, or both, are 'on' and TR3 or TR4, or both, are 'off'. The low resistance channel of TR1 or TR2 to earth provides a LOW output (logic 0). The logic operation of the NOR gate is summarized in Table 1.3.

Inputs		States				Output
A	B	TR1	TR2	TR3	TR4	F
LOW	LOW	OFF	OFF	ON	ON	HIGH
LOW	HIGH	OFF	ON	OFF	ON	LOW
HIGH	LOW	ON	OFF	ON	OFF	LOW
HIGH	HIGH	ON	ON	OFF	OFF	LOW

Table 1.3 NOR gate operation

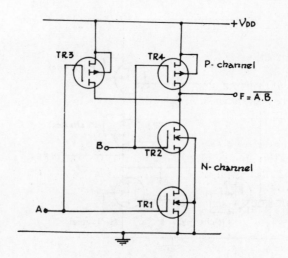

Fig. 1.31 CMOS NAND gate.

An equivalent circuit for a CMOS NAND gate is given in Fig. 1.31 and Table 1.4 summarizes its operation.

Inputs			States			Output
A	B	TR1	TR2	TR3	TR4	F
LOW	LOW	OFF	OFF	ON	ON	HIGH
LOW	HIGH	OFF	ON	ON	OFF	HIGH
HIGH	LOW	ON	OFF	OFF	ON	HIGH
HIGH	HIGH	ON	ON	OFF	OFF	LOW

Table 1.4 NAND gate operation

The CMOS logic family can operate with supply voltages ranging from about 3–15V and produce a high noise immunity of about 0·4 of the supply voltage. If the supply voltage is +5V, then CMOS is TTL compatible. The fan-out is very high (>50) and the quiescent power dissipation is extemely small at only a few nanowatts rising to a few milliwatts when switching from one state to another. The propagation delay is about 30ns per gate allowing a toggle speed of 10MHz.

HCMOS (High Performance or High Speed)
The scaling-down process referred to under HMOS has also been applied to CMOS devices where the p-channel and n-channel devices are scaled

equally to produce minature, high speed CMOS for use in V.L.S.I. HCMOS operates with supply voltages of between 2 to 6V and offers the high noise margin associated with CMOS. They have a small propagation delay of about 9ns, a very low power dissipation (14μW at 10kHz rising to 14mW at 10MHz) and a high fan-out. Compared to Advanced Schottky TTL, HCMOS has a slightly longer propagation delay but gives a 1000 reduction in power consumption and offers a high input impedance and a large output drive.

CMOS Transmission Gate

CMOS offers some unique circuit configuration and one example is given in Fig. 1.32 of a **Transmission Gate** or **Bilateral Switch**. Complementary transistors TR1 and TR2 act as a switch between points Y and Z permitting the transmission of signals in either direction and TR3, TR4 act as an inverter stage.

When the enable terminal(E) is in the LOW state at 0V, both TR1 and TR2 are 'off' and there is an open-circuit between Y and Z. The 'off' state leakage current between Y and Z is about 200nA(max). With the enable terminal in the HIGH state at $+V_{DD}$, TR1 and TR2 are both 'on' forming a low resistance channel between Y and Z of about 300ohm (with V_{DD} at $+5$V). This bilateral switch may be used to switch both digital and analogue signals providing that they do not exceed V_{DD} or fall below 0V, with propagation delays of the order of 10ns. Typical applications include switching in sample and hold circuits and mutiplexers.

A typical transmission gate i.c. is the 4066 which is a Quad Bilateral Switch having an 'on' resistance typically between 60 to 350ohm with an input signal equal to V_{DD}.

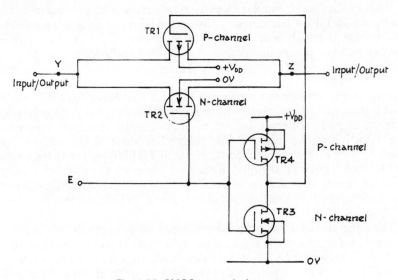

Fig. 1.32 CMOS transmission gate.

CMOS (4000 series) Typical Parameters

Supply Voltage	3–18V
Temperature Range	−40 to +85°C

Supply Voltage = 5V (at 25°C)

Input voltage HIGH, V_{IH}	3·5V (min) to 5V (max)
Input voltage LOW, V_{IL}	0V (min) to 1·5V (max)
Output voltage HIGH, V_{OH}	4V (min)
Output voltage LOW, V_{OL}	0·5V (max)
D.C. Noise margin	1·45V
Input current HIGH, I_{IL}	0·3μA
Input current LOW, I_{IL}	0·3μA
Output current HIGH, I_{OH}	−0·7mA
Output current LOW, I_{OL}	0·8mA

Integrated Injection Logic (I^2L)

The reasons why MOS devices have predominated in LSI, and VLSI chips is that:

(a) They require a smaller area of fabrication than bipolar devices.
(b) They dissipate less power than bipolar devices.
(c) Bipolar devices require isolation diffusion which wastes chip area.
(d) MOS devices may be used as load resistors whereas in bipolar circuits diffused resistors are used which take up more area than the bipolar transistor.

On the other hand, bipolar gates have a much smaller propagation delay than their MOSFET counterparts. Integated injection logic was introduced to combine the high speed of bipolar technology with the high packing density and low power dissipation of MOSFET technology.

Basic I^2L Gate

A basic I^2L gate circuit is given in Fig. 1.33(a). Here a p-n-n transistor TR1 injects a constant current which is either steered into or away from the base of a multi-collector transistor TR2. In the structure diagram of Fig. 1.33(b) it will be seen that TR1 collector is common to the base of TR2 (both require p-regions) and that the base of TR1 is common to the emitter of TR2 (both require n-regions). Because of these structural features and the fact that identical structures on the same chip are self-isolating also that there are no resistors used, results in a very small fabrication area for a single I^2L gate.

The injection current is supplied to the gate via a resistor(R) which may be internal or external to the silicon chip. This single resistor is used to supply the injection current for all of the gates on the chip via a common rail. The speed of operation can be varied over a wide range by altering the injection current by means of adjusting the value of R.

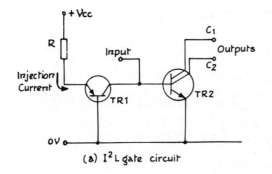

(a) I^2L gate circuit

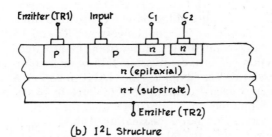

(b) I^2L Structure

Fig. 1.33 Basic I^2L gate.

I^2L NOR and NAND Gates

An equivalent circuit for a NOR gate is given in Fig. 1.34 where the constant current transistor for each basic gate has been omitted. The multi-collector transistors TR1 and TR2 act as inverters with a pull-up resistor Rp connected between the commoned outputs and +Vcc.

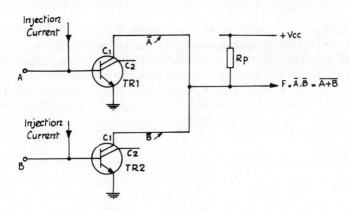

Fig. 1.34 I^2L NOR gate.

With a LOW input (50mV) applied to both TR1 and TR2, the injection currents are diverted away from their respective bases and both transistors will be 'off'. Under this condition with Vcc at +5V the commoned output will be HIGH. When a LOW (50mV) is applied to, say TR1 input and a HIGH (750mV) is applied to TR2 input, the injection current is diverted away from TR1 base but steered into TR2 base. Thus TR1 is 'off' and TR2 is 'on'. Thus the output will be LOW at a level depending upon the value of the pull-up resistor. With Vcc at +5V the output is compatible with TTL. However, since the I^2L input logic levels are small (logic $0 = 50mV$ and logic $1 = 750mV$), TTL can only drive I^2L if the TTL logic drive levels are attenuated. Note that if the C_2 outputs are commoned using an additional pull-up resistor the fan-out of the circuit is enhanced.

The equivalent circuit for a NAND gate is shown in Fig. 1.35 which illustrates the versatility of the basic I^2L structure. Inverters TR1 and TR2 supply their outputs to additional inverters TR3 and TR4 which have their open-collectors commoned. This arrangement effectively provides the AND function. A further inverter TR5 with its output connected by a pull-up resistor to Vcc completes the NAND function. Note the availability of the other collector outputs of TR1–TR4 to produce additional logic functions using other inverter gates within the chip.

I^2L offers a very low power dissipation of about $100\mu W$ per gate and a high packing density of up to 200 gates per square millimeter or chip area. The propagation delay attainable is at present of the order of 1–8ns but the noise margin is only 350mV.

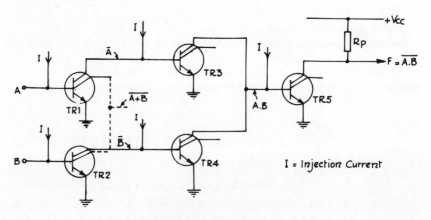

Fig. 1.35 I^2L NAND gate.

CHAPTER TWO

M.S.I. DIGITAL CIRCUITS

INTEGRATED CIRCUITS THAT are used in the design of digital systems can be classified according to the number of gates per chip as indicated by Table 2.1 **Small Scale Integrated circuits** are packages incorporating logic gates and flip-flops, *etc* and may be regarded as the basic building blocks of digital systems. **Medium Scale Integrated circuits** are essentially **digital sub-systems** into which are fabricated items such as multiplexers, decoders, registers, adders, *etc*. **Large Scale** and **Very Large Scale Integrated circuits** on the other hand may be regarded as complete digital systems, *e.g.* microprocessors, memories, controllers, *etc*. In this chapter we will be considering a large number of digital circuits many of which are MSI digital sub-systems in their own right but a few which are also available in SSI.

Classification	Number of Logic Gates per i.c.
S.S.I	3–30
M.S.I.	30–300
L.S.I.	300–3000
V.L.S.I.	>3000

Table 2.1 Approximate I.C. Gate Densities

SEQUENTIAL LOGIC CIRCUITS

In sequential logic circuits the output depends upon digital signals which have already been applied to the system over some previous period of time. A sequential system must therefore possess some 'storage' or 'memory' device.

Bistable Elements

A **bistable** is a simple memory or storage element which has two stable states. Once the device has been put into one of the states, it will remain in that state until a suitable signal is applied to cause it to change to the other stable state. If the power supply is disrupted, the state to which the bistable will return when power is restored is indeterminate. The bistable element is able to store one bit of binary information but this type of memory element is said to be **volatile**, since the stored information is lost when the power supply is removed.

In digital electronics bistable elements are also referred to as **flip-flop**, although the bistable oscillator and monostable oscillator (flip-flop) are disimilar in operation. However, since manufacturers often adopt the US Military Standard which uses the name 'flip-flop' for the bistable element both labels will apply to the same element in this chapter.

Bistable/Flip-Flop Symbols

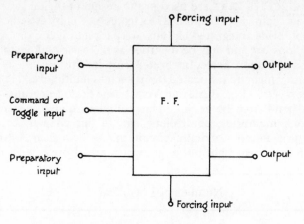

Fig. 2.1 General bistable/flip-flop symbol.

Output: There may be 1 output terminal(Q) or 2 (Q1 and Q2). If there are 2, the 'output state' refers to the states of the signals at Q1 and Q2; since these are normally complementary, the state at Q is usually considered to represent the output state. Since when there are 2 outputs and they are complementary, they are usually labelled Q and $\bar{Q}$.

Preparatory Input (e.g. J,K,D): This is an input terminal to which the application of an active signal does not cause a change of the output state, but prepares the circuit for such a change.

Command Input: An input terminal to which the application of an active signal causes the output to assume the state corresponding to the preparatory inputs. It is also known as the 'clock' input terminal.

Toggle Input: An input terminal at which an active transition from one state to the other directly causes a change in the output state of the flip-flop.

Forcing Input: An input terminal to which the application of an active signal directly causes the output to assume a specific state, irrespective of the states of the other input terminals. These terminals are often labelled 'direct set' and 'direct reset'.

The above strict definitions are taken from the Military Standard but variations of these will be found in practice. A full appreciation of the various inputs will be realised when the actual devices are studied in detail.

S-R Flip-Flop

The general symbol for an S-R flip-flop is shown in Fig. 2.2(a). It may be constructed from 2 cross-coupled NOR gates as in Fig. 2.2(b). With an S-R flip-flop the output Q is set at logic 1 when a logic 1 is applied to the S terminal. This is true irrespective of the previous state of Q. At the same time $\bar{Q}$ will assume a logic 0 condition. Thus the S terminal may be regarded as the terminal which permits the Q output to be SET to logic 1. In a similar way, the application of a logic 1 to the R terminal results in the output at Q being RESET to the logic 0 state, irrespective of its previous state. Thus the R terminal may be regarded as the terminal which permits the Q output to be RESET to the logic 0 state. Thus the flip-flop is often called the SET-RESET flip-flop.

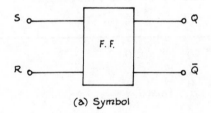

(a) Symbol

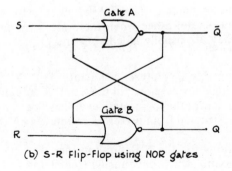

(b) S-R Flip-Flop using NOR gates

Fig. 2.2 S-R flip-flop.

Considering Fig. 2.2(b), the operation is as follows. Assume that initially $Q = 0$ ($\bar{Q} = 1$) and that S and R are both held at logic 0. It will be seen that this is a stable operating condition since both inputs to Gate A will be at logic 0 producing a logic 1 at the gate output and that the inputs to Gate B will be complementary producing a logic 0 at the gate output, *i.e.* Q holds $\bar{Q}$ at logic 1 whilst $\bar{Q}$ holds Q at logic 0.

Suppose now that the S terminal is set at logic 1 (the R terminal remaining at logic 0). The application of a logic 1 at the S terminal causes the $\bar{Q}$ output to change to logic 0. This results in both inputs of Gate B becoming logic 0, hence Q changes its state to logic 1. If S is now returned to logic 0, the circuit remains with Q at logic 1 which is the other stable state of the flip-flop. The signal applied to the S terminal need only be applied momentarily since the feedback between gates causes the flip-flop to **memorise** the last instruction. Note that the application of a further logic 1 pulse to the S terminal has no further effect once Q is set at logic 1. Using similar reasoning it can be shown that if a logic 1 is applied to the R terminal with $S = 0$, the Q output will be reset to logic 0.

It is important to note that the simultaneous application of a logic 1 to the S and R terminals must be avoided. Under this condition both Q and $\bar{Q}$ will be at logic 0 and the final output will be indeterminate, depending upon the relative switching speed of the two gates. A truth table for the S-R flip-flop is given in Table 2.2.

S	R	Q_n	Q_{n+1}
0	0	0	0
0	0	1	1
1	0	0	1
1	0	1	1
0	1	0	0
0	1	1	0
1	1	0	? output state
1	1	1	? indeterminate

Table 2.2 Truth Table of S-R Flip-Flop

In the above truth table Q_n represents the state of the Q output prior to the application of the logic levels shown in the S and R columns and Q_{n+1} the state of the Q output after the logic input levels have been applied. The S-R flip-flop may be constructed from two cross-coupled NAND gates as shown in Fig. 2.3

Typical applications for the S-R flip-flop include temporary store for binary information and switch debouncing (see chapter 5). The basic S-R flip-flop, although limited in application in its own right, forms the basis of other more sophisticated bistable elements.

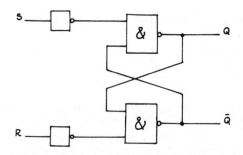

Fig. 2.3 S–R flip-flop using NAND gates.

Clocked S-R Flip-Flop

It is often desirable to synchronously control all operations in a digital system and this may be done by using a 'synchronising' or 'clock' pulse. By using a clock pulse it is possible to 'gate' or 'clock' signals into the F.F. at some precise instant in time. Symbols for the clocked S-R flip-flop are given in Fig. 2.4. The signals applied to the F.F. may be gated with the clock pulse

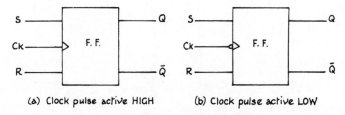

(a) Clock pulse active HIGH   (b) Clock pulse active LOW

Fig. 2.4 Symbol for clocked S–R flip-flop.

in the HIGH state, diagram (a) or in the LOW state, diagram (b). A possible logic circuit for a clocked S-R flip-flop (clock pulse active HIGH) is given in Fig. 2.5.

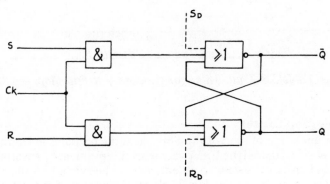

Fig. 2.5 Clocked S–R flip-flop.

When the clock pulse (Ck) is LOW, the outputs of the AND gates will also be LOW and the F.F. will be in one of its stable states. Changes in the logic levels at the S and R inputs will have no effect on the output state of the F.F. When the clock input goes HIGH (logic 1), the outputs of the AND gates assume the logic states of the S and R inputs thereby permitting the F.F. outputs to change accordingly.

Additional inputs S_D and R_D may be provided. These are **forcing** inputs and may be used to set or reset the flip-flop independently of the logic states of the S, R and Ck inputs. For example if the Q output is at logic 0 and the inputs from the AND gates are also at logic 0, then with $S_D = 1$ and $R_D = 0$ the Q output will be set at logic 1. Conversely with Q initially at logic 1, the application of $S_D = 0$ and $R_D = 1$ will set the Q output at logic 0. The S and R forcing inputs are also known as the PRESET (PR) and CLEAR (CLR) terminals respectively. A truth table for the clocked S-R flip-flop is given in Table 2.3.

Ck	S	R	Q_n	Q_{n+1}	
0	0	0	0	0	
0	0	0	1	1	
0	0	1	0	0	
0	0	1	1	1	
0	1	0	0	0	
0	1	0	1	1	
0	1	1	0	0	
0	1	1	1	1	
1	0	0	0	0	
1	0	0	1	1	
1	0	1	0	0	
1	0	1	1	0	
1	1	0	0	1	
1	1	0	1	1	
1	1	1	0	?	
1	1	1	1	?	indeterminate

Table 2.3 Truth Table for Clocked S-R Flip-Flop

D-Type Flip-Flop (Latch)

A major limitation of the S-R flip-flop is that the output is indeterminate when S = R = 1. The D-type F.F. overcomes this problem by ensuring that the S and R inputs are always complementary. The symbol for the D-type flip-flop is shown in Fig. 2.6 and Fig. 2.7 illustrates a method of construction. There is now only 1 input, the D-input (D stands for data) and the flip-flop

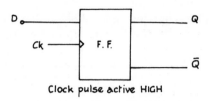

Fig. 2.6 Symbol for D-type flip-flop.

uses clocking. It will be seen that the NOT gate ensures that the inputs to. the NOR gates are always complementary thus the hazard that exists when S = R = 1 has been removed.

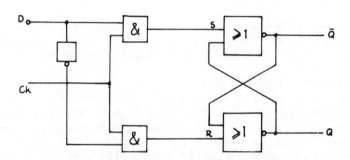

Fig. 2.7 A method of producing a D-type flip-flop.

The waveforms of Fig. 2.8 illustrate the basic action of this flip-flop. In Fig. 2.8(a) when the clock pulse is in the high state, the data input is at logic 1 thus the Q output of Fig. 2.7 is SET at logic 1, *i.e.* the same as the input data. Conversely if the input data is at logic 0 when the clock pulse goes HIGH as in Fig. 2.8(b), the Q output will be RESET at logic 0, *i.e.* the same as the input data. Thus the Q output of a D-type flip-flop 'latches' onto the input

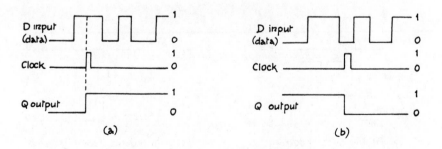

Fig. 2.8 Clocking data into the Q output.

data when a clock pulse is applied and will retain that data until new data is clocked-in. A truth table for the D-type flip-flop is given in Table 2.4.

Ck	D	Q_n	Q_{n+1}
0	0	0	0
0	0	1	1
0	1	0	0
0	1	1	1
1	0	0	0
1	0	1	0
1	1	0	1
1	1	1	1

Table 2.4 Truth Table for D-type Flip-Flop

Edge-Triggered D-Type Flip-Flop

If the clocking arrangement used in the flip-flop allows data to be clocked into the output during the time period that the clock pulse is in the HIGH state (level triggering), then if the input data changed during this period the output would change. To avoid this, the period of a data bit must be greater than the clock pulse period (t) as in Fig. 2.9(a). However, this would limit the rate at which the input data is allowed to change its state.

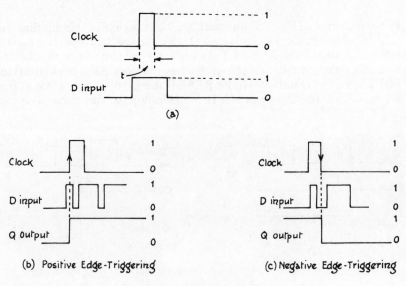

(a)

(b) Positive Edge-Triggering   (c) Negative Edge-Triggering

Fig. 2.9 Edge-triggering.

The problem may be overcome by only allowing the transfer of data to the output on the edge of the clock pulse. Either the leading edge (positive-edge triggering) or the trailing edge (negative-edge triggering) of the clock pulse may be employed as illustrated in Figs. 2.9(b) and (c). Input data can then change state during the clock pulse interval without the output data changing. With edge-triggering the speed of clocking is very fast and occurs at a specified voltage level between logic 0 and logic 1 on the leading or trailing edge of the clock pulse.

In manufacturers data the D-type F.F. is listed sometimes as a D-type F.F. (Signetics 54/74175 Quad D-type flip-flop) or as a latch (Signetics 54/7475 Quad Latch). The operational difference between them is that with the 'latch' the output will follow the D input as long as the clock pulse is at the high level, whereas with the 'D-type F.F.' data is only transferred to the output on the edge of the clock pulse.

Use of the D-type F.F. as a Memory Cell

An elementary form of memory cell using a D-type F.F. as a store for a single bit of data is shown in Fig. 2.10. When the read/write line is in the LOW state, the output of G1 will follow the binary signal applied to the 'data-in' line which is applied to the D-input of the F.F. Also, the output of G2 will pass the clock signal to the clock input of the F.F. Thus assuming level triggering, when the clock pulse goes HIGH, the data from G1 is clocked into the Q output. At the end of the clock pulse period, the data (a logic 1 or logic 0) is stored in the F.F.

To output the data held in the F.F. the read/write line is placed in the HIGH state thus inhibiting G1 and G2. However, when a clock pulse is applied to G3 the output from this gate will follow the data bit held in the Q output of the F.F. Note that reading the data from the F.F. does not alter the data stored (non-destructive read-out).

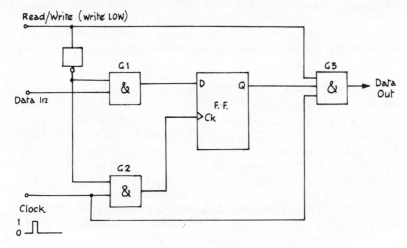

Fig. 2.10 Use of a clocked D-type flip-flop as a memory cell.

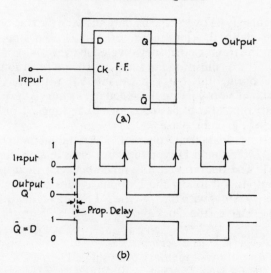

Fig. 2.11 Use of D-type F.F. as a divide-by-two stage.

Use of a D-type F.F. as a Divide-by-two Stage

If the Q output of a D-type F.F. is fed back to the D input as shown in Fig. 2.11(a), the F.F. will operate as a divide-by-two stage providing the propagation delay of the F.F. is greater than the period required for triggering. Waveforms illustrating the operation are given in Fig. 2.11(b).

Consider that initially that the $\bar{Q}$ output is at logic 1, *i.e.* Q = 0. When the first input pulse is applied (which acts as the clock) and assuming positive-edge triggering, the $\bar{Q}$ output which is the D input will be clocked into the Q output and the $\bar{Q}$ output will go to logic 0. On the positive-going edge of the next input pulse, the Q output will be set at logic 0 and the $\bar{Q}$ at logic 1 and so on. It will be seen that the output pulses have a frequency that is one-half of the input pulse frequency. The circuit can be described as a 'toggled' F.F. since the output **toggles** (changes state) for each input pulse.

Pin-Out and Logic Diagrams

D-type flip-flops are available in TTL and CMOS i.c. technology and the example given in Fig. 2.12 is for the Signetics M.S.I. Quad Bistable Latch 8275. The 8275 is a Schottky TTL Quad Latch employing D-type flip-flops. The pin-out diagram is given in Fig. 2.12(a). Separate 'enable' lines to latches 1-2 and 3-4 permit individual control of each pair of latches. The 'enable' pulse acts like a clock pulse and initially data is transferred on the leading edge of the pulse. Whilst the enable pulse is in the HIGH state, the output Q follows the data input. When the enable pulse falls, the input data is retained at the Q output. Both Q and $\bar{Q}$ are accessible. The logic diagram for each latch is given in Fig. 2.12(b).

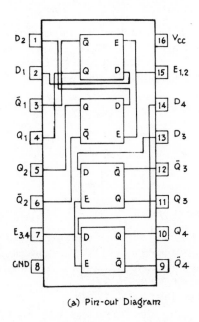

(a) Pin-out Diagram

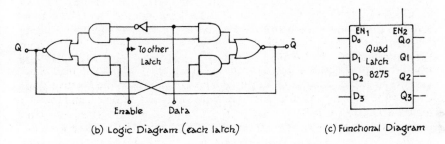

(b) Logic Diagram (each latch)   (c) Functional Diagram

Fig. 2.12 Pin-out and logic diagrams of signetics M.S.I. quad bistable latch 8275.

In diagrams of digital systems it is usual to represent M.S.I. circuits with a functional diagram, see Fig. 2.12(c). M.S.I. logic elements are represented by rectangular blocks with inputs and outputs on opposite faces of the longer sides and generally control inputs on one of the faces of the shorter sides. A small circle at an input means that the specific input is active LOW, similarly a small circle at an output means that the output is active LOW. More recently manufacturers have adopted a different form of functional logic symbol diagram based on the IEEE/IEC recommendations (see J-K flip-flops).

J-K Flip-Flop

The J-K flip-flop is essentially an S-R F.F. with additional logic circuitry to eliminate the indeterminate output that occurs when S = R = 1. The logic symbol is given in Fig. 2.13 and one possible circuit arrangement in Fig. 2.14. The flip-flop is provided with 2 input terminals (J and K); these are

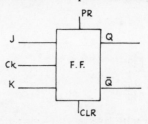

Fig. 2.13 J–K flip-flop symbol.

preparatory inputs. It is a clocked F.F. and direct set and reset may also be provided (PR and CLR). Feedback from the Q and Q̄ outputs and the 2 AND gates provide a **clock steering function** and the condition J = K = 1 is now permissable producing a predictable output.

It will be seen that the Q and Q̄ output states, as well as the preparatory inputs J and K, determine which input of the basic S-R flip-flop receives the clock pulse. For example consider that initially Q = 0 and Q̄ = 1, a logic 1 is applied to J and a logic 0 to the K input. Because of the feedback, then when a clock pulse is applied (active HIGH) the upper AND gate will be operative and the lower AND gate inoperative. Thus the logic states of J and K are transferred to the S and R inputs of the basic S-R flip-flop, setting the Q output to logic 1 and the Q̄ output to logic 0. If now a logic 1 is applied to the K input and a logic 0 to the J input then on the next clock pulse the lower AND gate will be made operative and the upper AND gate will be inoperative. As a result, the Q output will be reset to logic 0 and the Q̄ output to logic 1. In principle the results set out in the truth table of Table 2.5 will apply.

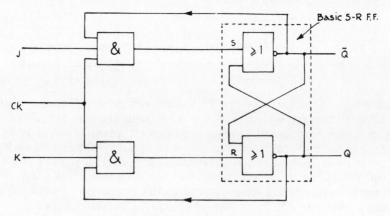

Fig. 2.14 J–K flip-flop circuit arrangement.

| J | K | Q output | |
		Before Clock Pulse	After Clock Pulse
0	0	0	0
0	0	1	1
0	1	0	0
0	1	1	0
1	0	0	1
1	0	1	1
1	1	0	1
1	1	1	0

Table 2.5 Truth table for J-K Flip-Flop

The table illustrates the versatility of the J-K Flip-Flop which may be summarised as follows:

(1) If J = K = 0 there will be no change in the output state when a clock pulse is applied (the F.F. is then in the HOLD condition).
(2) If J = 1, K = 0 then Q output is placed in the 1 state and the $\bar{Q}$ in the 0 state when a clock pulse is applied (the F.F. is then in the SET condition).
(3) If J = 0, K = 1 the Q output is placed in the 0 state and the $\bar{Q}$ in the 1 state when a clock pulse is applied (the F.F. is then in the RESET condition).
(4) If J = K = 1, the Q and $\bar{Q}$ outputs reverse states on the receipt of each clock pulse (the F.F. is then in the TOGGLING mode).

It will therefore be appreciated that there are more modes of operation available due to the use of the two preparatory inputs J and K. A circuit based on the use of NAND gates is given in Fig. 2.15.

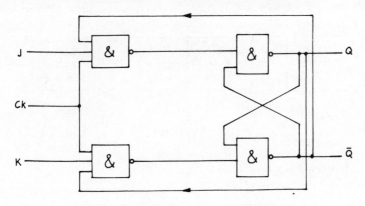

Fig. 2.15 J–K flip-flop using NAND gates.

Race-Around Condition

If the Q and Q̄ outputs of the J-K flip-flop change state before the end of the clock pulse, the input conditions to the AND steering gates of Fig. 2.14 will change. The effect is that Q oscillates between 0 and 1 for the duration of the clock pulse, see Fig. 2.16, and at the end of the clock pulse period the output is indeterminate. The condition can be avoided if the clock pulse

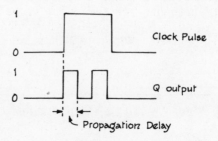

Fig. 2.16 Oscillation of Q output when propagation delay is short compared with clock pulse period.

period is short compared with the propagation delay of the F.F., a requirement which is rarely met in practice with modern high speed i.cs. This 'race-around' condition led to the development of the Master-Salve flip-flop.

Master-Slave J-K Flip-Flop

This type of J-K flip-flop does not suffer from the 'race-around' condition and the basic idea of its operation is illustrated by Fig. 2.17. There are now 2 flip-flops, the 'Master' and the 'Slave' with the Slave driven from the Master. The switches S1 and S2 are arranged so that when S1 is closed, S2 is open and vice versa. On the leading edge of the clock pulse S1 is closed and the input is clocked into the output of the Master. At this time the Slave flip-flop will not

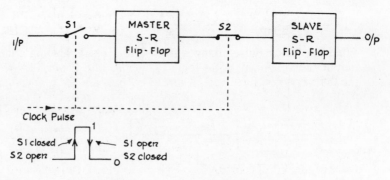

Fig. 2.17 Basic idea of master–slave principle.

change since switch S2 is open. When the clock pulse changes state once more on its trailing edge, S1 opens disconnecting the input from the Master. At the same time, since S2 is closed the output of the Slave is made to follow the output of the Master. Because S1 is open, any feedback applied in an actual circuit cannot affect the output of the Master.

It will now be shown how this basic principle is applied to the J-K flip-flop, a circuit arrangement of which is given in Fig. 2.18. As with the basic J-K flip-flop feedback is applied from the output (of the SLAVE) to the clock steering gates A and B. This configuration eliminates the 'race-around' condition and a predictable output results for the condition $J = K = 1$.

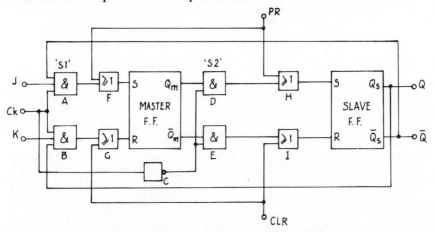

Fig. 2.18 Arrangement for master–slave J–K flip-flop.

Operation

The AND gates A and B effectively replace 'S1' of Fig. 2.17 and the AND gates D and E replace 'S2'. When the clock pulse goes to logic 1 on its leading edge, the Master F.F. is enabled via gates A and B but due to the inverter gate C, the Slave F.F. is disabled. The following initial conditions will be assumed:

$$Qs = 0 \ , \ Qm = 0 \ , \ J = K = 1, \text{Clock pulse} = 0 \text{ and PR} = 0$$
$$\bar{Q}s = 1 \ , \ \bar{Q}m = 1 \qquad\qquad\qquad\qquad\qquad\qquad CLR = 0$$

(1) When the clock pulse changes from 0 to 1 on its leading edge, the output of gate A will go to logic 1, but the gate B output will be in the logic 0 state. Since gate A and B outputs are the S and R inputs of the Master F.F., the Qm output of the Master will be set at logic 1 ($\bar{Q}m = 0$). At this time the Slave F.F. is disabled as gates D and E are inoperative.

(2) When the clock pulse changes from logic 1 to logic 0 on its trailing edge, gates A and B are disabled, but gates D and E are enabled. Thus the Qm and $\bar{Q}m$ outputs of the Master F.F. become the inputs of the Slave F.F., *i.e.* Qs goes to logic 1 and $\bar{Q}s$ goes to logic 0. The change in the

output states of the Slave F.F. have no effect on the Master since gates A and B are inoperative.

(3)   On the leading edge of the next clock pulse when it goes from logic 0 to logic 1, the output of gate A is set at 0 and the output of gate B to logic 1. This resets the Master F.F. outputs to Qm = 0 and Q̄m = 1. On the trailing edge of the clock pulse, the Slave F.F. follows the Master and the Slave outputs are reset to Qs = 0, Q̄s = 1. When the Master-Slave F.F. is operated in this way it is said to be a 'toggle' flip-flop (T flip-flop). Waveforms summarising the modes of operation of the Master-Slave F.F. are illustrated in Fig. 2.19.

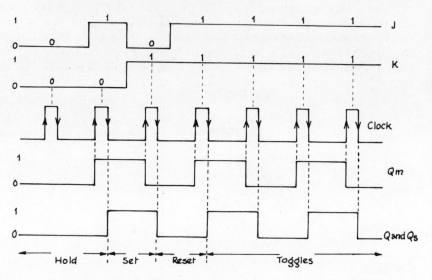

Fig. 2.19 Waveforms showing operation of master–slave J–K flip-flop.

The J-K F.F. is a very important and flexible logic device and forms the basis of counting circuits which are considered in the next section. Fig. 2.20(a) and (b) show how T and D-type flip-flops may be constructed from a J-K flip-flop. The T-type F.F. is constructed by tying the J and K terminals

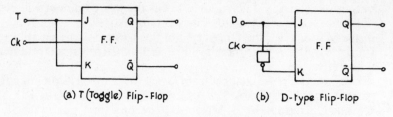

(a) T (Toggle) Flip - Flop   (b)   D-type Flip-Flop

Fig. 2.20 T and D-type flip-flops constructed from a J–K flip-flop.

together (the T-terminal). When T is at logic 0, the state of the flip-flop will not change when the clock input goes to logic 1. However when T is at logic 1, the flip-flop will toggle each time the clock input goes to logic 1. A D-type F.F. is constructed by arranging that the J and K inputs are always complementary by the use of the inverter gate.

Pin-Out and Logic Diagrams

Pin-out and functional diagrams for the Texas Instruments SN54ALS112A Dual J-K Flip-Flops are given in Fig. 2.21. This i.c. package contains 2 independent negative-edge-triggered J-K flip-flops with Clear and Preset. When the Preset and Clear are inactive (HIGH), data at the J and K terminals is transferred to the outputs on the negative-going edge of the clock pulse. A LOW level at the Clear or Preset, resets or sets the outputs regardless of the logic levels on the other inputs. A pin-out diagram

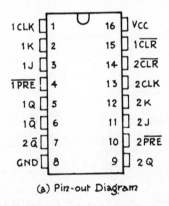

(a) Pin-out Diagram

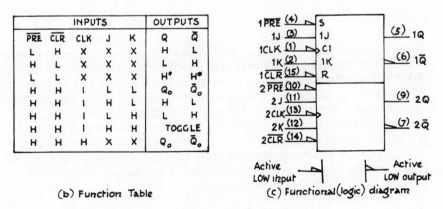

	INPUTS				OUTPUTS	
$\overline{PRE}$	$\overline{CLR}$	CLK	J	K	Q	$\overline{Q}$
L	H	X	X	X	H	L
H	L	X	X	X	L	H
L	L	X	X	X	H*	H*
H	H	I	L	L	Q_0	$\overline{Q}_0$
H	H	I	H	L	H	L
H	H	I	L	H	L	H
H	H	I	H	H	TOGGLE	
H	H	H	X	X	Q_0	$\overline{Q}_0$

(b) Function Table

(c) Functional (logic) diagram

Fig. 2.21 Pin-out and functional diagrams of Texas Instruments dual J–K edge triggered flip-flops.

is given in Fig. 2.21(a) and a functional table in Fig. 2.21(b). Note that in the table 'X' means 'don't care' or 'it does not matter what state the particular input is in'.

The functional diagram given in Fig. 2.21(c) conforms to IEEE/IEC standards for logic symbols. A rectangular outline block is used with inputs on the left separated from outputs on the right. The main rectangle is divided into 2 smaller rectangles each containing identical J-K flip-flops in this case. Active LOW inputs or outputs are indicated by the small triangle symbols with a corresponding negation sign over the label outside, *e.g.* 1PRE (Preset LOW, Flip-Flop 1).

When with a particular logic device the control inputs such as Clock, Preset or Clear *etc* are common to **all** of the logic devices within the i.c. package, the functional diagram is normally shown as illustrated in Fig. 2.22. Here a common control block with a distinctive outline is used with the **common** control signals applied to it which control the 4 separate elements of the circuit, assumed to be D-type flip-flops for this example.

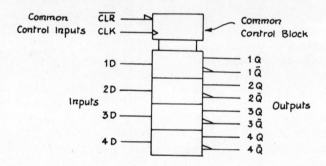

Fig. 2.22 Use of common control block in functional logic diagrams (IEEE/IEC).

COUNTERS

Asynchronous Binary Counter

A common method of procucing a binary counter is to use a number of Master-Slave J-K flip-flops wired as 'toggle' flip-flops as shown in Fig. 2.23. The pulses to be counted are applied to the clock input of flip-flop A and it will be seen that the output of flip-flop A provides the clock input to flip-flop B, the output of flip-flop B provides the clock input to flip-flop C and so on. Negative-edge triggering is used, *i.e.* the 'slave' output of any flip-flop changes state on the negative-going edge of its clock input. A common 'clear' line (clear LOW) is used to reset all Q outputs LOW. During counting the 'clear' line is held in the HIGH state. With this particular circuit both Q and Q̄ outputs are made available, but this is not always the case.

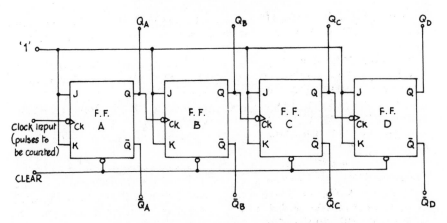

Fig. 2.23 Asynchronous binary counter (Modulo-16).

Operation

Assume that the counter has been reset by taking the 'clear' line LOW, *i.e.* $Q_A - Q_D$ outputs will all be LOW (logic 0). The waveforms given in Fig. 2.24 depict the operation during counting. On the leading edge of the first clock pulse the 'Master' of flip-flop A will be set at logic 1 and on the trailing edge, the logic 1 from the 'Master' will be transferred to the output of the 'Slave', *i.e.* Q_A will be set at logic 1. Since the Q output is the clock input of flip-flop B, the 'Master' of flip-flop B will be set at logic 1 (but not its 'Slave') at this time. Thus at the end of the first clock pulse, the binary output of the counter will be 0001 (note that Q_A provides the least significant digit.)

On the leading edge of the second clock pulse the Master of flip-flop A will be reset to logic 0 and on the trailing edge of the clock pulse the Slave of flip-flop A will be reset to logic 0. It will be remembered that the Master of flip-flop B has already been set at logic 1, thus when the Q_A output goes LOW, the Slave of flip-flop B will be set to logic 1. Since the output of flip-flop B is connected to the input of flip-flop C, the Master of flip-flop C will be set to logic 1 (the Slave of C will not change until the output of flip-flop B goes LOW). Thus at the end of clock pulse 2, the output of the counter will be 0010.

On the leading edge of the third clock pulse, the Master of flip-flop A will be set at logic 1 and on the trailing edge of the Slave of flip-flop A will be set at logic 1. Q_A will change from logic 0 to logic 1 and the Master of flip-flop B will be reset to logic 0. At the end of clock pulse 3, the output of the counter will be 0011. This procedure continues and at the end of 15 clock pulses the counter output will be 1111. Upon receipt of clock pulse 16, the counter will be reset to 0000.

Modulus

Any number of flip-flops can be cascaded in this way to form an n-bit counter. The arrangement of Fig. 2.23 is referred to as a 4-bit counter since

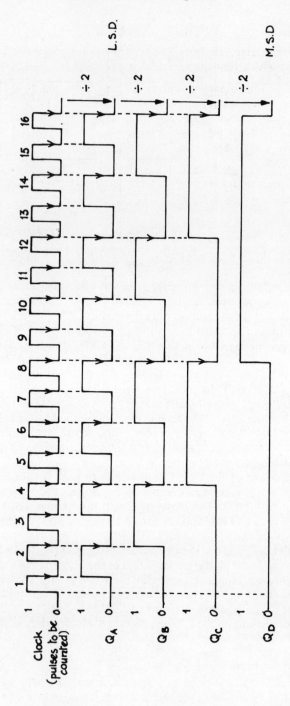

Fig. 2.24 Waveforms showing operation of asynchronous counter of Fig. 2.23.

there are 4 binary bits or digits in the coded output. A 5-bit binary counter will count up to decimal 31 and reset on clock pulse 32, but requires 5 flip-flops of course. The modulus of a binary number system is the decimal equivalent which that number of bits or digits can represent, *e.g.*

3-bit binary counter = 2^3 = 8 .... Modulo-8
4-bit binary counter = 2^4 = 16 .... Modulo-16
8-bit binary counter = 2^8 = 256 .... Modulo-256

Propagation Delay

In practice there is a small delay between the application of a clock pulse to any stage of a counter and its output assuming the appropriate logic level as illustrated in Fig. 2.25.

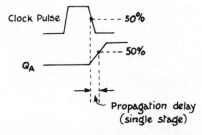

Fig. 2.25 Maximum counting rate limited by propagation delay.

With an **asynchronous** counter or 'ripple' counter, the flip-flops do not change state at the same instant causing the propagation delays to become accumulative. For example when the counter output is 0111 then on the eighth clock pulse all the flip-flops change state. However Q_D cannot change until Q_C changes, Q_C cannot change until Q_B changes and Q_B cannot change until Q_A changes. Thus, if the propagation delay of each stage is 20ns, a time delay of 80ns will elapse before the counter output finally settles to 1000.

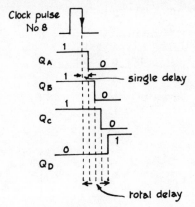

Fig. 2.26 Diagram showing accumulative delays.

Because the change of state appears to 'ripple' through the counter, the asynchronous counter is also known as a **ripple-counter**. Waveforms illustrating the effect of acuumulative delays when the counter output changes from 0111 to 1000 are given in Fig. 2.26. Note that the individual outputs settle in their new state at different time instants. Often the counter outputs are used to operate gates and the delay can cause false gate operation if the counter is operated at too high a speed.

Bidirectional Binary Counter

The asynchronous binary counter previously described is a FORWARD counter or an UP counter since it counts 'up' from zero. It is often required to be able to count 'down' from a pre-determined value to zero. A counter operating in this mode is referred to as a DOWN counter or REVERSE counter. From the truth table given in Table 2.6 it will be seen that the **total** value stored in both Q and $\bar{Q}$ at the end of any clock pulse is constant and equal to decimal 15. Clearly the previous counter will count 'down' if the $\bar{Q}$ outputs are used. By using suitable combinational logic a **Bi-Directional** counter may be constructed. One possible circuit arrangement is given in Fig. 2.27.

Clock pulse No.	Output States										
	Q_D	Q_C	Q_B	Q_A			$\bar{Q}_D$	$\bar{Q}_C$	$\bar{Q}_B$	$\bar{Q}_A$
0 (16)	0	0	0	0			1	1	1	1
1	0	0	0	1			1	1	1	0
2	0	0	1	0	Count 'Up'	Count 'Down'	1	1	0	1
3	0	0	1	1			1	1	0	0
4	0	1	0	0			1	0	1	1
5	0	1	0	1			1	0	1	0
6	0	1	1	0	↓	↓	1	0	0	1
7	0	1	1	1			1	0	0	0
8	1	0	0	0			0	1	1	1
9	1	0	0	1			0	1	1	0
10	1	0	1	0			0	1	0	1
11	1	0	1	1			0	1	0	0
12	1	1	0	0			0	0	1	1
13	1	1	0	1			0	0	1	0
14	1	1	1	0			0	0	0	1
15	1	1	1	1			0	0	0	0

Table 2.6 Truth table for 4-bit counter of Fig. 2.23.

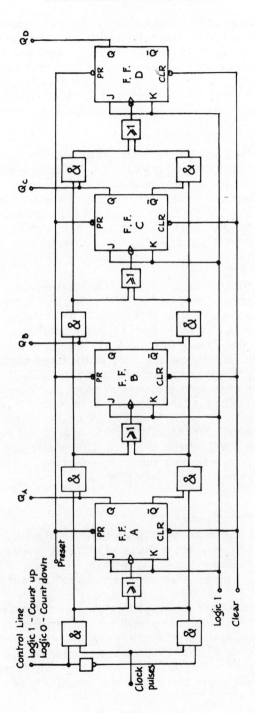

Fig. 2.27 Reversible (up-down) counter.

To provide the reversible function with a single counter it is necessary to introduce a control line as shown. When the control line is set at logic 1 the upper set of AND gates are enabled but the lower set of AND gates are disabled (by the inverter gate) and the counter is in the UP count mode. When the control line is set at logic 0, the upper set of AND gates are disabled but the lower set are enabled; the counter is then in the DOWN count mode.

Count Up Mode

The control line will be held at logic 1 and if the clear line is taken LOW the counter outputs will all be reset at logic 0. The clear line is then taken HIGH. When the clock pulses (the pulses to be counted) are applied at the counter input, the counter will count up as previously described for Fig. 2.23 with the upper set of AND gates connecting the Q output of each F.F. to the clock input of the following F.F. via an OR gate. After 15 clock pulses the counter will register 1111 at its outputs.

Count DOWN Mode

If now the control line is taken to logic 0, the counter will count down from 1111. On the leading edge of the first clock pulse, the Ck input of flip-flop A will go HIGH and the Master of flip-flop A will be reset. The Ck input of flip-flop B will remain LOW since $\bar{Q}_A$ is logic 0. On the trailing edge of the clock pulse, the Slave of flip-flop A will be reset to logic 0 and $\bar{Q}_A$ will change to logic 1. Throughout this interval, the Ck input of flip-flop B has remained LOW. The counter output is now 1110.

On the leading edge of the second clock pulse, the Ck input of flip-flop A will go HIGH and the Master will be set. At the same time the Ck input of flip-flop B will go HIGH and its Master will be reset to logic 0. On the trailing edge of the clock pulse, the Slave of flip-flop A will be set to logic 1 and the Slave of flip-flop B will be reset to logic 0. The counter output is now 1101. This operation continues down the counter with the counter output being decremented by one for each clock pulse input.

Synchronous Binary Counter

In synchronous counters the counting sequence is controlled by means of the pulses to be counted which clocks **all** of the flip-flops together so that changes in the output states occur in synchronism. This effectively eliminates the large propagation delay associated with asynchronous counters.

Master-slave flip-flops are invariably used to avoid the possibility of oscillation and instability when feedback connections are made in the complete counter. In the synchronous mode of operation, the appropriate input signals are gated into the Masters of all the flip-flops in the counter on the leading edge of the clock pulse. On the trailing edge of the clock pulse the new values of the count are transmitted synchronously to the flip-flop outputs.

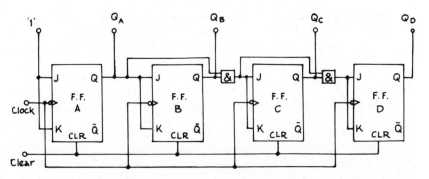

Fig. 2.28 4-bit synchronous counter Modulo-16.

One method of producing a synchronous binary counter is given in Fig. 2.28. It will be noted that the clock pulses (pulses to be counted) are fed directly to each flip-flop in the counter and that the J and K inputs are tied together but only in flip-flop A are they connected to logic 1. The J and K inputs of flip-flop B are connected to the Q output of flip-flop A, but the J and K inputs of flip-flops C and D are driven from AND gates which are supplied with signals from the input and output of the previous stage.

Circuit Operation

Assume that the counter has been initially cleared so that the binary output is 0000. On the leading edge of the first clock pulse, the Master of A will be set to logic 1. Since the J and K inputs of all other flip-flops are at logic 0, the Masters of these flip-flops will not change. On the trailing edge of the clock pulse the Slave of flip-flop A will be set at logic 1, thus the binary output will be 0001.

On the leading edge of the second clock pulse, the Master of flip-flop A will be reset to logic 0. Since Q_A is at logic 1, the Master of flip-flop B will be set to logic 1. Flip-flops C and D will be unchanged. On the trailing edge of the clock pulse, the Slave of A will be reset to logic 0 and the Slave of B will be set to logic 1. The counter output will then be 0010.

On the leading edge of the third clock pulse, the Master of A will be set at logic 1. Since Q_A is at logic 0, flip-flop B will not be affected which is also true for flip-flops C and D. On the trailing edge of the clock pulse, the Slave of A will be set to logic 1. The counter output will then be 0011.

On the leading edge of the fourth clock pulse the Masters of flip-flops A and B are reset to logic 0. Since both Q_A and Q_B are at logic 1, the Master of C will be set at logic 1. On the trailing edge of the clock pulse, the Slaves of A and B will be reset to logic 0, whilst the Slave of C will be set at logic 1. The counter output is now 0100. It will be seen that the ripple-through delay has been removed and the outputs of the flip-flops change in synchronism. The propagation delay is the same for all stages of the counter and is equal to the propagation delay of one flip-flop. Reversible synchronous counters may also be constructed.

Divide-By-N Counter

It is often desirable to be able to count to a base N which is not a power of 2. For example, to count to a base of 10 is a common requirement as this is the basis of the denary number system of which we are more familiar.

Decade Counter

For a decade or divide-by-ten counter we require a chain of n bistables such that n is the smallest number for which $2^n > N$, e.g. for $N = 10$ (decade counter), $n = 4$. A feedback gate is then added so that on a count of 10 all outputs are reset to logic 0. Inspection of the truth table for a binary counter shows that at a count of 10 the output states are:

$$Q_D = 1, Q_C = 0, Q_B = 1 \text{ and } Q_A = 0 \ (1010).$$

For a decade counter, however, we require **all** of the outputs to be in the logic 0 state at a count of 10, i.e. the Q_D and Q_B outputs must be reset back to logic 0 at a count of 10. One way of achieving this is as shown in Fig. 2.29.

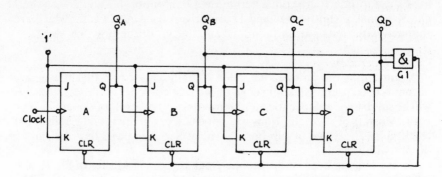

Fig. 2.29 Asynchronous decade counter.

The 4 flip-flop stages are wired as toggle flip-flops with the pulses to be counted applied to the first stage. When a count of 1010 is reached, the output from the NAND gate G1 goes LOW which is applied to the 'clear' inputs of all stages, resetting all outputs to logic 0. The timing waveforms for the counter are shown in Fig. 2.30. Note that on the tenth input pulse the counter outputs are all at logic 0; this is providing that the propagation delay (reset time) of the CLEAR inputs is short (typically 50ns for TTL devices). Unequal reset times from the CLEAR to the output of individual flip-flops may cause unreliable operation, e.g. if flip-flop B has a shorter reset time than flip-flop D, then flip-flop B input to G1 will go LOW before flip-flop D input with the result that flip-flop D will not clear. It will be seen that counting sequence recommences on the eleventh input pulse.

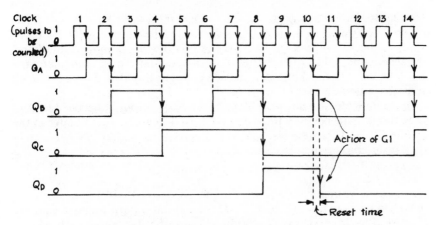

Fig. 2.30 Timing waveforms for decade counter.

Use of Decade Counter

A number of decade counters may be arranged to give a decimal read-out using 7 segment displays. It will be appreciated, of course, that although a decade counter counts input pulses from 0 to 9 and then resets on the tenth pulse, the actual read-out from the flip-flop stages is in **binary**.

The basic principle of a 3-digit display is illustrated in Fig. 2.31. Three separate counters are employed arranged as the 'Units', 'Tens' and

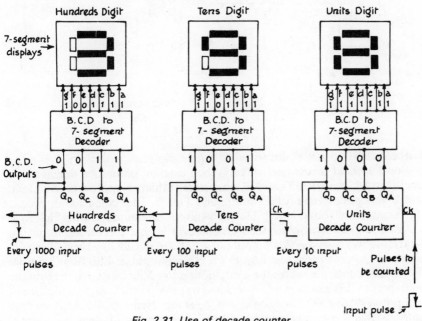

Fig. 2.31 Use of decade counter.

'Hundreds' decade counters, thus providing binary-coded decimal (B.C.D) outputs. The pulses to be counted are applied to the clock input of the 'units' counter, the Q_D output of which is used as the clock input of the 'tens' decade counter. The Q_D output of the 'tens' counter is then used to provide the clock input fo the 'hundreds' decade counter; this idea may be extended to increase the number of digits used in the display.

To operate the 7-segment displays the counter outputs must be 'decoded' using 4-7 line decoders, which are considered in greater detail later in the chapter. The diagram shows the decoder output states after 398 input pulses have been applied to the 'units' counter.

Divide-by-five Counter

A similar arrangement may be used to produce a divide-by-five counter and a circuit is given in Fig. 2.32. Here 3 bistables are required and are connected in the toggling mode. On a count of 5 the outputs will be:

$$Q_A = 1, Q_B = 0 \text{ and } Q_C = 1.$$

However, on a count of 5 we require all outputs to be LOW. This is ensured when on a count of 101, G1 operates forcing the clear inputs LOW thus resetting all outputs to logic 0. Counters may be reset at any maximum value using the above method.

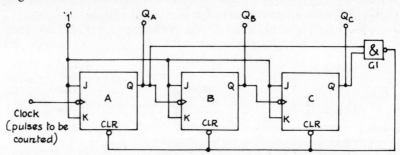

Fig. 2.32 Divide-by-five asynchronous counter.

Synchronous Decade Counter

The design of a counter which is to divide by a number that is not a multiple of 2 is more difficult for synchronous than asynchronous counters. Additional logic circuitry is required and a circuit of a synchronous decade UP counter is given in Fig. 2.33 which should be compared with Fig. 2.28.

As for the asynchronous decade counter it is required for all outputs to return to logic 0 on the tenth input pulse. The feedback line from $\bar{Q}_D$ to G1 prevents Q_B going to logic 1 on the tenth input pulse. Flip-flop D output must change to logic 1 after the eigth input pulse but return to logic 0 on the tenth pulse. This requirement is satisfied by providing a logic 1 on the J input of flip-flop D from G3 and a logic 1 on the K input from Q_A after the seventh pulse, so that flip-flop D toggles on the eigth pulse, $i.e.$ Q_D becomes logic 1.

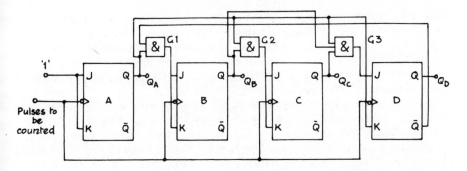

Fig. 2.33 Circuit arrangement for synchronous decade counter.

However, after the ninth pulse, the K input of flip-flop D goes to logic 1 and the J input to logic 0 so that on the tenth pulse Q_D is reset to logic 0. Synchronous decade counters are available commercially, such as the SN74ALS192 4-bit synchronous UP/DOWN counter.

Programmable Counter

A programmable counter is one which can be made to 'clear' all outputs on reaching any of a number of predetermined counts. The basic principle is shown in Fig. 2.34 where the gates G1–G10 form a comparator. The binary

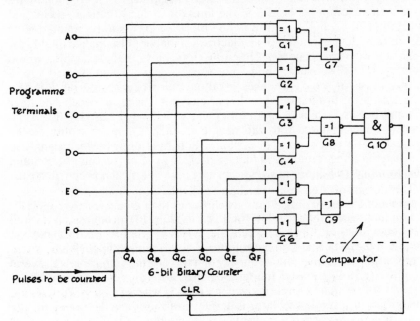

Fig. 2.34 Basic principle of programmable counter.

count at which the counter should be reset is specified by applying appropriate binary signals (logic 1s and 0s) to the programming terminals A–F; there will be one programming terminal for each 'bit' of the counter and here a 6-bit counter is used in the example. When the $Q_A - Q_F$ outputs of the counter match the logic signals on the programming terminals the output of G10 will go LOW which is applied to the CLEAR input of the counter thereby resetting all outputs to logic 0. The counter will then count up again until the programmed count has been reached when again the counter will reset once more and so on.

With, say, $A = B = C = 1$ and $D = E = F = 0$, the counter will reset on the seventh input pulse producing a divide-by-seven counter or if $A = B = E = 1$ and $C = D = F = 0$ the counter will reset on the nineteenth pulse resulting in divide-by-nineteen counter. The logic signals applied to the programming terminals may be 'hard-wired', come from a switch selector or be supplied from a programmed ROM via latches.

Counter Applications

Counters are extensively used in industrial control systems, digital computers and data communication and the following describes the main applications.

Straight Counting

The application of electronic counters in industrial proceses predominates over human counters because of the limitations due to fatigue, speed and reliability. In 'straight' counting, the objects or events to be counted must first initiate the generation of an electrical signal or pulse that is suitable for application to the counter. This may be achieved, for example, where objects on a conveyer belt interrupt a light beam sensed by a photo-transistor, which produces an output pulse for each interruption. The counter may be programmed so that when it has reached a specified number of input pulses, it delivers an output pulse which may be used to divert the objects being counted into the next container. There versatility of the programmable counter may be exploited here by altering the logic signals on the programming terminals so that, say, 24, 36 or 72 objects may be counted into containers of different sizes according to the particular production run.

Frequency Division

We have seen that a 4-bit counter (modulo-16) produces an overall frequency division of 16 between the pulses applied to the first and the output of the last bistable in the counter. There are many applications where it is desirable to change the frequency of a waveform, or to generate several frequencies from 1 master timing oscillator, and counters may be used for these purposes. An example is given in Fig. 2.35 where frequency division of the output of a stable oscillator is employed to produce the timing for the seconds, minutes and hours displays of a digital clock. The hours 'units' counter is a programmable one operating either as a divide-by-ten or

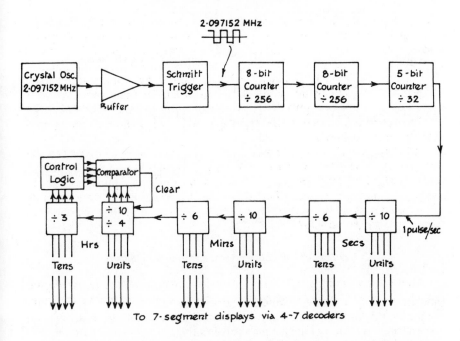

Fig. 2.35 *Frequency division using counters to produce timing for 24 hour digital clock.*

divide-by-four counter. When the hours 'tens' counter is registering either 0 or 1 then the control logic provides the appropriate binary signals to the comparator so that the hours 'units' counter operates as a divide-by-ten stage. If, however, the hours 'tens' counter is registering a 2, the control logic supplies binary signals to the comparator such that the hours 'units' counter operates as a divide-by-four stage. This permits the hours counters to be reset to 00 on reaching 24 hours.

Frequency and Time Measurement

The basic principle showing how a counter may be utilised for the measurement of frequency is illustrated in Fig. 2.36. A stable crystal oscillator operating at a frequency of, say, 1MHz is divided down (counters may be used for this purpose) to produce pulses at 1Hz which are applied to the clock input of a J-K flip-flop wired in the toggling mode. The Q output of the flip-flop is thus HIGH for a 1 second period and LOW for the following 1 second period.

The signal whose frequency is to be measured is converted into logic pulses having 1 and 0 levels by means of a zero-crossing detector. These pulses are applied through the AND gate to the counter when the Q output of the flip-flop is in the HIGH state. Since the AND gate is active for a known

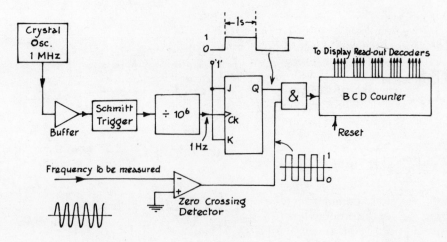

Fig. 2.36 Use of counter for measuring frequency.

time interval of 1 second, which is accurately maintained by the crystal oscillator, the number of pulses counted by the counter in this time interval gives a true indication of the frequency (directly in Hz). A similar principle is used to measure the time interval between pulses as illustrated by Fig. 2.37.

In this arrangement the counter counts a number of pulses of known frequency from a stable oscillator source during the interval between pulses. The first pulse (pulse A) is applied to the SET input of an S-R flip-flop which sets the Q output HIGH and the second pulse (pulse B) is applied to the RESET input which causes the Q output to go LOW. Thus the AND gate is

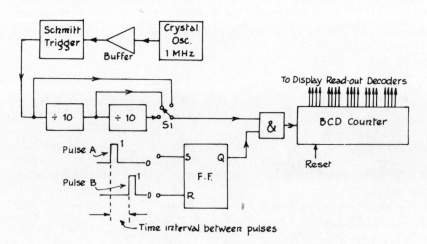

Fig. 2.37 Use of counter to measure the time interval between pulses.

made active during the interval between pulses when it passes pulses of known frequency to the counter from the range time selector switch S1. The number of pulses counted during this interval gives a direct indication of the time measurement; the read-out display may be calibrated in secs, ms, μs or ns *etc.*

For example, if the counter registers say, 216 pulses with pulses at a frequency of 100kHz applied (S1 in the position shown) during the period that the AND gate is active, then the time interval between pulse A and pulse B would be

$$216 \times \frac{1}{10^5} \text{ secs} = 2 \cdot 16 \text{ ms.}$$

The shorter the time interval to be measured the higher will be the frequency of the pulses applied from the range time selector switch. To measure time intervals of the order of tens of nano-seconds, the frequency of the oscillator would need to be much higher, say, 100MHz.

Speed Measurement

The rotational speed of a shaft may be measured by converting it into a time measurement as illustrated in Fig. 2.38. For each revolution of the shaft one pulse is induced into the coil by the permanent magnet attached to the disc. If the number of pulses are counted in a fixed period of, say, 1 second the rotational speed of the shaft in revs/sec may be ascertained. This measuring technique uses the same principle as for the determination of frequency shown in Fig. 2.36.

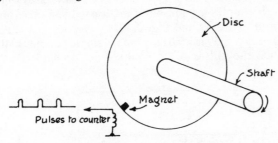

Fig. 2.38 Use of counter for measuring rotational speed of shaft.

Similarly, if an object passes between 2 light source – photo sensor arrangements set at a fixed distance apart, the average speed of the object is inversely proportional to the time interval between the generated pulses from the light source – photo sensor combinations. Thus by measuring the time interval between the generated pulses using the arrangement of Fig. 2.37, the speed of the object over the fixed distance may be determined.

Digital Computing

In a digital computer a central processing unit (c.p.u.) carries out the sequence of instructions fed into the computer from disc or tape and stored in the programme memory. As each instruction of the programme is executed, a counter (programme counter) is used to count the instructions and to automatically fetch the next instruction from the programme memory thus ensuring that the c.p.u. deals with the instructions in the strict sequence that they appear in the programme.

Counters may also be incorporated into peripheral A-D converter chips that provide the computer with appropriate digital signals from external transducers.

Pin-Out and Logic Diagrams

Integrated circuit counters are fabricated using both TTL and CMOS technology and asynchronous, synchronous, binary or B.C.D. versions are available. TTL counters are generally limited to 4-stages (modulo-16) per package but the number of count stages may be increased by cascoding counters of the same family. The asynchronous counters that are available are all up-counters; the reversible (up/down) counter is only available with synchronous counters.

Because of the greater packing density of CMOS a larger number of counter stages can be accommodated in a single i.c. package and 7-stage, 12-stage and 14-stage counters are available in the CMOS range. The very low power consumption of CMOS counters makes them attractive for use in digital watches and clocks and a 21-stage counter is available for this application. CMOS counters on the other hand do not have such a high maximum count rate as TTL, typically 10MHz for CMOS as opposed to 30MHz for TTL. Examples of pin-out functional diagrams for CMOS counters are given in Fig. 2.39 and Fig. 2.40.

The HEF4024B of Fig. 2.39 is a 7-stage binary ripple counter with a clock input ($\overline{CP}$) to which the pulses to be counted are applied. The counter

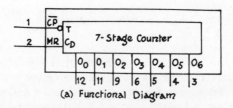

(a) Functional Diagram

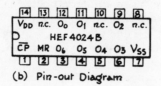

(b) Pin-out Diagram

Fig. 2.39 MSI 7-stage asynchronous binary counter.

advances on a HIGH-to-LOW transistion of each clock pulse (count-up). An overriding master reset input (MR) resets all outputs LOW when a HIGH is placed on the MR line independent of the state of the clock input. The 7 counter outputs O_0 - O_6 are fully buffered and each counter stage operates as a static toggle flip-flop.

The HEF4029B of Fig. 2.40 is a 4-stage synchronous, edge triggered binary/decade counter (up/down). A HIGH on the UP/$\overline{DN}$ line places the counter in the count-up mode and a LOW in the count-down mode. The counter is provided with a count-enable input ($\overline{CE}$) which enables the counter when the $\overline{CE}$ line is LOW. It is also provided with a parallel load input PL which will load information on the P_0 – P_3 lines when the PL line is HIGH. The counter will increment or decrement on the LOW-to-HIGH transition of the clock pulse CP when both the $\overline{CE}$ and PL lines are LOW.

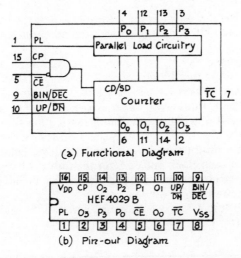

(a) Functional Diagram

(b) Pin-out Diagram

Fig. 2.40 MSI 4-stage synchronous up/down counter.

With a HIGH on the BIN/$\overline{DEC}$ line the counter operates as a binary counter and will reset on a count of 16. When a LOW is placed on the BIN-$\overline{DEC}$ line the counter operates as a decade counter and will reset on a count of 10. The $\overline{TC}$ terminal signal is normally HIGH but goes LOW when the counter reaches its maximum count in the up-count mode or minimum count in the down-count mode provided $\overline{CE}$ is LOW. Parallel buffered outputs are available on O_0 – O_3.

REGISTERS

When a number of bistables are connected together so that they store related data, the assembly is referred to as a **register**. A **shift register** is a register in which the data may be moved serially to the left or right and some types are reversible. A shift register is a temporary store of data. In a digital computer or system they are used to move data to and from a central memory or to store the interim results of arithmetic processes; the ability to shift data one place to the left or right is an essential requirement to some binary arithmetic operations. There are many arrangements for shift registers and some of the more common types will be considered.

Basic Shift Register

A basic shift register may be constructed from a series of D-type flip-flops as in Fig. 2.41 which illustrates a shift-right shift register. The operation is as follows:

1) Assume that all flip-flops have been reset so that the Q_A – Q_D outputs are at logic 0.

2) If the D input of flip-flop A is set at logic 1 then on the first clock pulse, the Q_A output will be set at logic 1 with the other outputs remaining at logic 0.

3) Assume that the data input is now returned to logic 0. On the second clock pulse the Q_A output will be set at logic 0 but since the output of flip-flop A was previously at logic 1 and is applied to the D input of flip-flop B, the Q_B output will be set at logic 1. The Q_C and Q_D outputs remain at logic 0. It will be seen that the logic 1 has shifted on place to the right.

4) The operation continues in this way with the logic 1 shifting one place to the right on each clock pulse. After the fifth clock pulse, the logic 1 will have shifted completely through the register and all outputs will be at logic 0; the register is now empty.

The truth table of Table 2.7 shows the propagation of the logic 1 though the register from left-to-right.

Clock Pulse No.	Q_A	Q_B	Q_C	Q_D
0	0	0	0	0
1	1	0	0	0
2	0	1	0	0
3	0	0	1	0
4	0	0	0	1
5	0	0	0	0

Table 2.7 Truth table for shift resister showing propagation of logic 1 from left to right

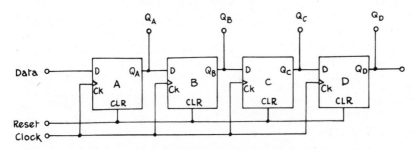

Fig. 2.41 Shift-right shift register.

In practice the input data to the register may consist of various combinations of logic 1s and 0s and the waveforms of Fig. 2.42 illustrate the propagation of the binary digits 1011 through the register of Fig. 2.41 assuming negative-edge triggering of the clock pulses. Note that after the fourth clock pulse has ended the 4-bits of data are stored in the register and will remain there provided clocking of the register ceases. To move the data serially out of the register, clocking must recommence and here it is assumed that it starts on the fifth clock pulse. At the end of the eighth clock pulse the data will have shifted completely through the register and all outputs will be at logic 0.

In this mode, the shift register operation may be described as **Serial In – Serial Out** (SISO). However, it should be noted that the data once clocked into the register is available in parallel form at the Q_A - Q_D outputs, thus the

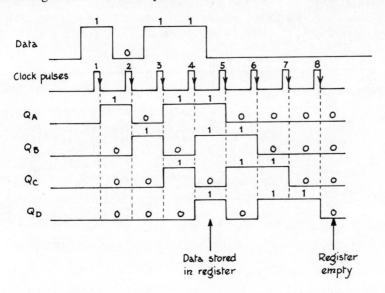

Fig. 2.42 Waveforms showing propagation of 1011 data through shift register.

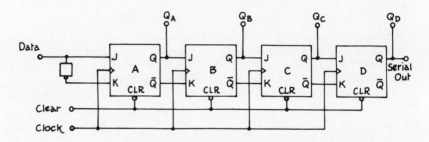

Fig. 2.43 4-bit shift register using J–K flip-flops.

shift register also provides a facility of **Serial In – Parallel Out** (SIPO). A 4-bit shift register may be implemented using J-K flip-flops as shown in Fig. 2.43. Here the J-K flip-flops are used as D-type flip-flops; note the complementary inputs to each stage of the register. The arrangement will operate in the SIPO and SISO modes.

Parallel Loading

It is often required to be able to load the register with parallel data, *i.e.* to load all of the bits into the register simultaneously. This is sometimes referred to as 'broadside' loading. A common example of this is in parallel-to-serial conversion; the data word is loaded into the register in parallel form then clocked out in serial form. There are many circuit arrangements for parallel loading and one example is given in Fig. 2.44.

The diagram shows a method of parallel loading using the 'forcing' inputs Preset and Clear. When the 'enable parallel-in' is LOW, the parallel data inputs A, B, C and D are inactive and the PR and CLR terminals are HIGH.

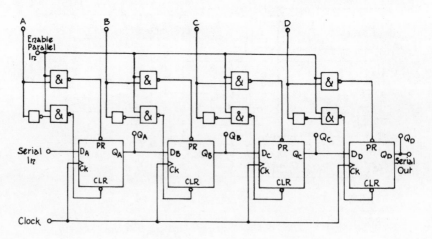

Fig. 2.44 Parallel loading of shift register.

The shift register then operates in the normal shift-right mode, the serial data input being D_A and the serial output data being Q_D. The data may also be read in parallel form once the register is loaded using outputs Q_A to Q_D.

A HIGH on the 'enable parallel-in' will permit parallel loading. Only input A need be examined since all the parallel inputs are the same. Suppose input A is HIGH (logic 1) when the enable line goes HIGH. This will cause the PR of flip-flop A to go LOW and the CLR to go HIGH. The flip-flop will be preset so that Q_A is HIGH (logic 1) irrespective of its previous state. Similarly when input A is LOW (logic 0) the PR of flip-flop A will go HIGH and the CLR will go LOW. The flip-flop will be reset so that Q_A is LOW (logic 0).

It is important to note that with this system a clock pulse is NOT required to parallel load the register. The shift register of Fig. 2.44 may be used in any one of the following modes:
(a)   Serial-In   / Serial-Out (SISO).
(b)   Serial-In   / Parallel-Out (SIPO).
(c)   Parallel-In / Serial-Out (PISO).
(d)   Parallel-In / Parallel-Out (PIPO).

The Reversible Shift Register

The shift registers previously considered are only capable of shifting data to the right. There are applications, however, where data shift to the right or left is desirable; we must therefore use a **reversible** shift register. The circuit diagram of Fig. 2.45 shows one arrangement of implementing a reversible S.I.S.O. shift register. It will be seen from the diagram that the principle of

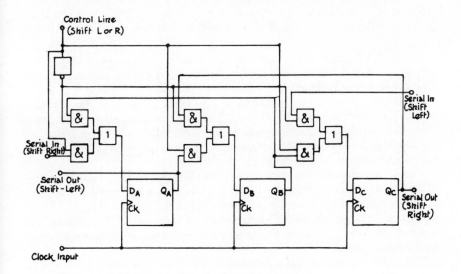

Fig. 2.45 Reversible shift register.

operation is unchanged. Under the control of the shift control line (logic 1 for right shift - logic 0 for left shift) the combinational logic gates effectively reverse the order of the flip-flops for left shift.

For left shift, the upper AND gates are made operative by the control line and the Serial In data from the shift left terminal is applied to the input of flip-flop C. The output of this flip-flop drives flip-flop B and so on. The left shift serial output is thus taken from flip-flop A. When right shift is selected the lower set of AND gates are made operative and the serial input is applied to the input of flip-flop A, the output of which drives flip-flop B and so on. Some reversible shift registers have the parallel loading facility previously referred to provide enhanced versatility.

The Ring Counter

Registers may be connected so that the data bits stored in the register may be **rotated**. A **ring counter** is basically a shift register whose input is obtained from its output as shown in Fig. 2.46.

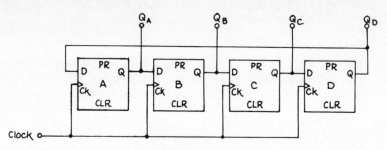

Fig. 2.46 Basic ring counter.

The diagram shows a 4-bit shift register utilising D-type flip-flops with the output of flip-flop D providing the input to flip-flop A. Suppose that initially flip-flop A output is set at logic 1 using the preset input and that the outputs of flip-flop B, C and D are reset to logic 0 using the clear input. The bits then stored in the register are as in Fig. 2.47(a). Each successive clock pulse will move the data in the register 1 place to the right and after the application of 4 clock pulses the logic 1 will have moves completely through the register and back to the output of flip-flop A.

With a ring counter, the state of the count after the appliction of a number of clock pulses is relatively easy to decode. By noting when a logic 1 appears at each flip-flop output, e.g. by means of a lamp, the state of the count can be noted; in fact no decoding is necessary. Counting by this method is, however, extravagant in flip-flop stages, i.e. 10-stages would be required for a decade counter.

When used in the manner described for Fig. 2.46, the ring counter will act as a divide-by-n circuit since the output of any given flip-flop stage will be at logic 1 for n clock pulses where n is the number of stages. Also, since the

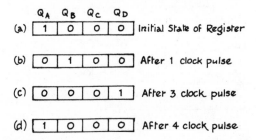

Fig. 2.47 Diagram showing operation of ring counter.

logic 1 pulse advances by one stage for each clock pulse, the ring counter outputs may be used where a set of sequential gating pulses are required to provide a stepping switch action.

A ring counter may be used to generate a repetitive pattern of bits as illustrated in Fig. 2.48. It may be arranged that each time the counter is switched on it is parallel loaded using the PRESET and CLEAR forcing inputs with, say, 8-bits when an 8-stage counter is employed. On the

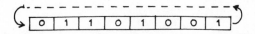

Fig. 2.48 Generation of repetitive pattern of bits using ring counter.

transition of each clock pulse the pattern of bits will move sequentially through the counter and the output from any stage will provide a serial train of bits of the desired pattern.

Twisted Ring Counter

The cycle length of a ring counter may be doubled by feeding back to the input from the $\bar{Q}$ output instead of the Q output. Such an arrangement is called a **twisted ring counter** and a circuit using J-K flip-flops is shown in Fig. 2.49(a) and its truth table in Fig. 2.49(b). If all of the outputs are initially set to logic 0 then the inputs to flip-flop A will be $J = 1, K = 0$. Thus on the first clock pulse the output of flip-flop A will be set at logic 1. On each succeeding clock pulse, this logic 1 state will move through the register and at the same time another logic 1 will be clocked into flip-flop A via the feedback from flip-flop D up to clock pulse no. 4. Since the output of flip-flop D changes state on clock pulse no. 4, then on the fifth clock pulse and succeeding clock pulses up to clock pulse number 7 a logic 0 will be clocked into the output of flip-flop A.

It should be noted that the output of the twisted ring counter is not in a binary code and will thus need decoding if this form of synchronous counting is to be used.

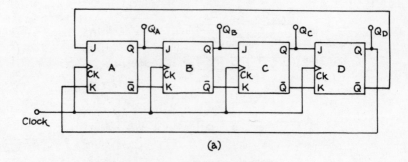

(a)

Clock Pulse No.	Q_A	Q_B	Q_C	Q_D
0	0	0	0	0
1	1	0	0	0
2	1	1	0	0
3	1	1	1	0
4	1	1	1	1
5	0	1	1	1
6	0	0	1	1
7	0	0	0	1
8	0	0	0	0

(b)

Fig. 2.49 A twisted ring counter, its circuit (a) and truth table (b).

Pin-Out and Logic Diagrams

Uses of the shift register inlcude the implementation of binary arithmetic, especially multiplication and division, where its versatility is enchanced by making it bidirectional, temporary storage (buffering) in data communication networks and it forms the basis of the Universal Asynchronous Receiver/Transmitter where the ability to provide parallel entry and parallel output is exploited in parallel-to-serial and serial-to-parallel conversion.

Shift registers are manufactured using both TTL and CMOS technology. The 4-bit register is the most common in TTL but 5-bit, 8-bit and 16-bit are also available. The high packing density of CMOS coupled with its low power consumption makes it an attractive proposition for registers with a very large number of bits, *e.g.* 64-bits but such registers are restricted to S.I.S.O. operation due to the limitations of the number of pin connections on the i.c. package. Some common registers are given in Table 2.8.

TTL

Type Number	Description
74LS194	4-bit Universal
74LS164	8-bit S.I.P.O.
74LS165	8-bit P.I.S.O.
74673	16-bit S.I.P.O.
74AS652	8-bit Transceiver and Register

CMOS

Type Number	Description
74164HCT	8-bit S.I.P.O.
74165HCT	8-bit P.I.S.O.
4015B	Dual 4-bit
4094B	8-bit with storage
4035B	4-bit Universal

Table 2.8 I.C. Registers.

CMOS HEF4035B MSI Shift Register

Examples of the pin-out functional diagrams of a MSI CMOS 4-bit register are given in Fig. 2.50. The HEF4035B has 4 synchronous parallel

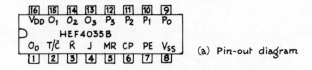

(a) Pin-out diagram

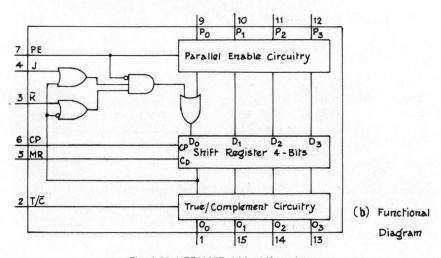

(b) Functional Diagram

Fig. 2.50 HEF4035B 4-bit shift register.

data inputs P_0 to P_3, 2 synchronous serial data inputs J and $\bar{K}$, a synchronous parallel enable input (PE) and buffered parallel outputs O_0 to O_3. It also features a true/complement input (T/$\bar{C}$) which when LOW will provide the complement of the stored data at the outputs. An overriding asynchronous master reset input (MR) is also provided. The shift register is edge-triggered on the positive-going transition of the clock pulse (CP). Each stage of the register is a D-type master/slave flip-flop.

The use of the 2 serial inputs J and $\bar{K}$ increase the versatility of the register. If J and $\bar{K}$ are connected together, then the first stage of the register will follow the data applied to the commoned input. This data may then be clocked serially through the register. If J is held at logic 1 and $\bar{K}$ at logic 0, then the first stage of the register will toggle (reverse state). On the other hand if J is held at logic 0 and $\bar{K}$ at logic 1, there will be no change in the state of the first stage (hold mode).

Advanced Schottky TTL 74AS652

The 74AS652 is a MSI transceiver/register incorporating two independent 8-bit registers and its pin-out diagram is given in Fig. 2.51. The device consists of bus transceiver circuits, D-type flip-flops and control circuitry

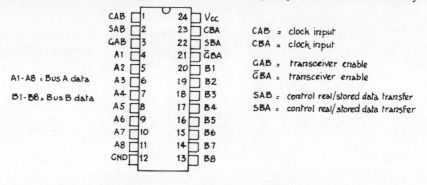

Fig. 2.51 Pin-out diagram of 74AS652.

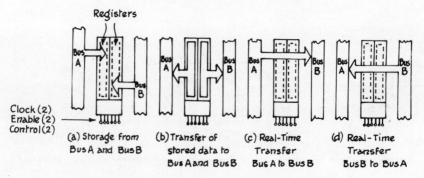

Fig. 2.52 Diagrams illustrating functions of 74AS652.

which are designed to permit multiplexed transmission of data directly from the data bus or from the internal storage registers. The diagrams of Fig. 2.52 illustrate the 4 fundamental functions that can be performed. It may be used to store data on the A and/or B data bus in the internal registers or transfer data from the internal registers to the data buses. Additionally, real-time transfer between data buses may also be achieved.

DECODERS

In digital systems, instructions as well as data are conveyed by binary digits. For example with a 4-bit binary signal, 2^4 or 16 instructions may be conveyed. A **decoder** is a combinational logic circuit that is used to decode or translate a number of input binary lines into a number of output lines where for a given binary input, **one** of the output lines remains HIGH all other lines being LOW or vice-versa.

2-To-4 Line Decoder
A simple arrangement is the 2-to-4 line decoder, a logic circuit of which is given in Fig. 2.53(a). The logic states shown on the diagram illustrate the

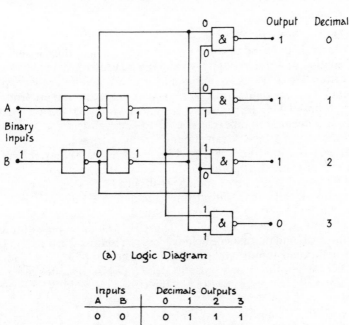

(a)   Logic Diagram

Inputs		Decimals Outputs			
A	B	0	1	2	3
0	0	0	1	1	1
0	1	1	0	1	1
1	0	1	1	0	1
1	1	1	1	1	0

(b)   Truth Table

Fig. 2.53 2–4 line decoder.

operation for a binary input of 11. In this arrangement a LOW (logic 0) is obtained on only 1 of the output lines for each binary code on the input, see the truth table of Fig. 2.53(b). Thus the presence of a logic 0 on a particular output line identifies the binary code on the input; this is the **decoding** process. The decoding process is essentially one of binary-to-decimal conversion, *i.e.* 2-line binary to 4-line decimal.

The idea of Fig. 2.53 may be extended to provide 8 output lines from 3 binary input lines using the same principle, but at the expense of an increase in the complexity in the number of logic gates used as illustrated in Fig. 2.54.

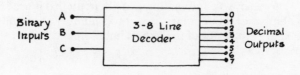

Fig. 2.54 3–8 line decoder.

B.C.D. To Decimal Decoder

With the B.C.D. numbering system each decimal digit is replaced by a combination of 4 binary digits which may be used to represent the decimal digits from 0 to 9. For each decade of the decimal number there will be one group of 4 binary digits, thus to represent decimal numbers from 0 to 999 three groups of 4 binary digits are needed. To translate the encoded B.C.D. digits into decimal numbers a B.C.D-to-decimal decoder is required and Fig. 2.55 shows a logic arrangement for this purpose.

For each decade, there will be 4 input lines and 10 output lines and the diagram illustrates the operation for a B.C.D. input equivalent to decimal 8. It will be seen that this input coding results in a LOW (logic 0) on the decimal 8 output line, all other output lines remaining HIGH (logic 1), *i.e.* this particular input coding has been identified.

Sometimes it is desirable to decode the B.C.D. input only during specific time intervals and this may be achieved by **strobing** as illustrated in Fig. 2.56. Here additional inputs are provided for the NAND gates and are tied together. When the strobe pulse is HIGH all NAND gates are active and decoding will take place, whereas if the strobe line is LOW the decoding is inhibited.

B.C.D. To 7-Segment Decoder

A B.C.D to 7-segment decoder has 4 input lines and 7 output lines and is formed from a combinational logic circuit. It is normally used to convert the B.C.D. output of a decade counter into a coded output that is suitable to operate the segments of a 7-segment l.e.d or liquid crystal display.

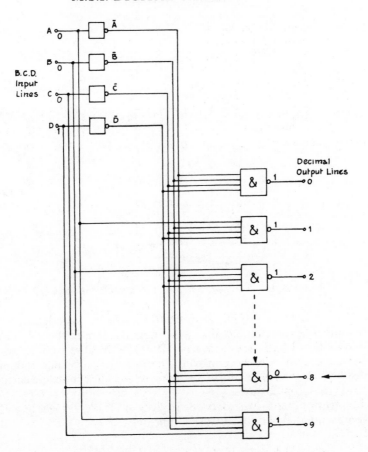

Fig. 2.55 B.C.D. to decimal decoder.

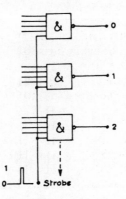

Fig. 2.56 Strobing the decoder.

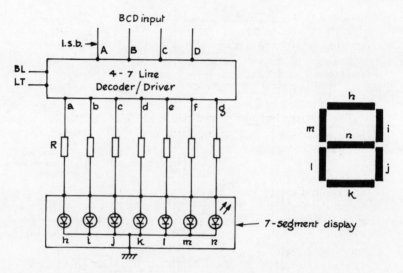

Fig. 2.57 B.C.D. to seven-segment decoder/driver for L.E.D. display.

The arrangement of Fig. 2.57 illustrates how the decoder/driver is used to operate a 7-segment l.e.d. display (common cathode type). When any of the output lines a–g of the decoder are HIGH (+5V), the l.e.d. array connected to that output is turned on which illuminates particular segments of the display. The series resistors (R) in the output lines limits the current in each l.e.d. to about 20mA.

A truth table for the decoder is given in Table 2.9 where a HIGH (H) represents +5V and a LOW(L) indicates 0V.

| Inputs | | | | | Outputs | | | | | |
D	C	B	A		a	b	c	d	e	f	g
L	L	L	L		H	H	H	H	H	H	L
L	L	L	H		L	H	H	L	L	L	L
L	L	H	L		H	H	L	H	H	L	H
L	L	H	H		H	H	H	H	L	L	H
L	H	L	L		L	H	H	L	L	H	H
L	H	L	H		H	L	H	H	L	H	H
L	H	H	L		H	L	H	H	H	H	H
L	H	H	H		H	H	H	L	L	H	L
H	L	L	L		H	H	H	H	H	H	H
H	L	L	H		H	H	H	H	L	H	H

Table 2.9 Truth Table for BCD-to-7-Segment Decoder

Two control inputs are provided on the decoder of Fig. 2.57. The L.T. (Lamp Test) terminal is used to check that all outputs go HIGH when the L.T. terminal is taken LOW. Under this condition all segments of the display should be illuminated thus displaying numeral 8. The L.T. terminal is a master input and overrides any other input to the decoder. The BL (Blanking) terminal input is used to place the decoder outputs a–g in the LOW state regardless of the state of the B.C.D. input and thus turn off the display. This control input is normally used to turn off leading zeros in a numeric display of digits, such as in a pocket calculator, to make the display easier to read and to reduce consumption.

Liquid Crystal Display

Liquid crystal displays are also 7-segment devices and will thus require a 4-7 line decoder for displaying numerals 0 to 9. When a voltage is applied between the Backplate (BP) and the segment, that particular segment is opaque (black). On the other hand if no p.d. exists between a sement and the backplate that segment is transparent.

To prevent chemical deterioration and hence increase life expectancy, the display is normally driven by a square-wave applied to the Phase(PH) input of the decoder, see Fig. 2.58. The diagram shows the logic states for an input that will result in the display of numeral 3. It will be noted that for this

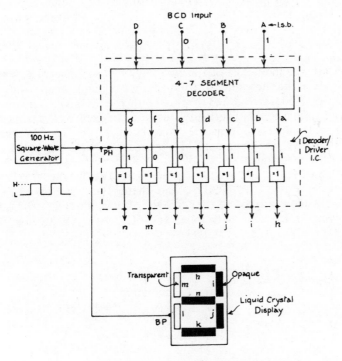

Fig. 2.58 Liquid crystal decoder/driver I.C.

condition the decoder outputs g and f are logic 1 and logic 0 respectively. These states are also shown in Fig. 2.59(a) and (b) together with the square wave input and output of the respective EX-OR gate. It will be seen that the square waves fed to the backplate and segment n are in antiphase, *i.e.* a p.d. exists between the backplate and segment n whereas the square waves fed to the backplate and segment m are in phase, *i.e.* no p.d. exists between the backplate and segment m. Thus segment n will be opaque and segment m transparent.

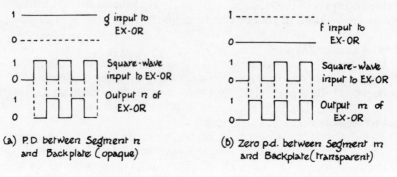

Fig. 2.59 Waveforms explaining operation of liquid crystal display.

MULTIPLEXERS

A multiplexer acts like a fast operating rotary switch connecting signals from various data channels one at a time into a common output line as illustrated in Fig. 2.60 which shows the basic principle. It is commonly used in data acquisition systems where the outputs of signal transducers are time-division multiplexed so that they may be processed by a common system and thus save on the amount of 'electronics' that is employed.

In practice the mechanical switch of Fig. 2.60 is replaced by electronic ones such as the CMOS switches shown in Fig. 2.61. The switches are closed one at a time in response to binary coded channel address signals. The output of the switches are fed to the load via a buffer amplifier to ensure maximum signal transfer. The channel address decoder is a binary-to-

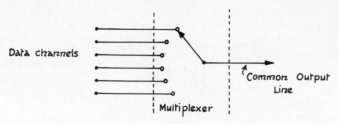

Fig. 2.60 Multiplexer principle.

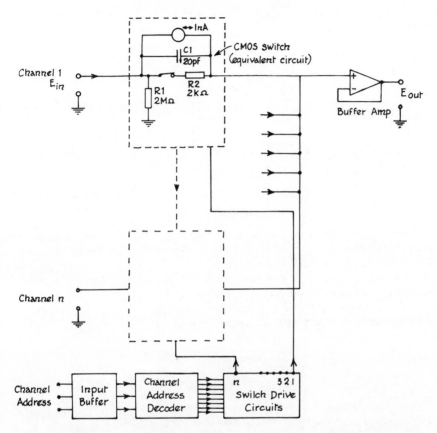

Fig. 2.61 Internal circuits of data signal multiplexer using CMOS switches.

decimal converter which is formed by a combinational logic circuit. An n-bit channel address will identify (select) 2^n channels, *e.g.* a 3-bit channel address will identify $2^3 = 8$ channels. The equivalent circuit of each CMOS switch includes R1 (the input resistance), R2 (the switch 'on' resistance), C1 (the 'on' capacitance) and a current generator representing the leakage current of the switch.

The data channels may be connected to the output in strict order as illustrated in Fig. 2.62 or the channel address may be programmed so that a particular channel(s) is switched to the output more frequently than others.

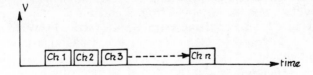

Fig. 2.62 Time-division multiplexed channel signals.

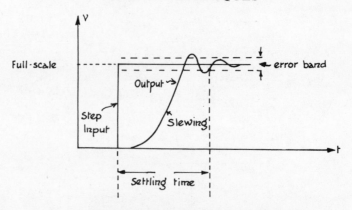

Fig. 2.63 Settling time of multiplexer.

The highest rate at which the multiplexer can switch from channel-to-channel at its specified accuracy is determined by its **settling time**, see Fig. 2.63. Settling time is defined as the time elapsing between the application of a full-scale step input to when the output enters and remains within a specified error band around the theoretical output for that input and is typically of the order of 3–4μs. For example the highest rate at which a multiplexer can switch with a settling time of 4μs,

$$= \frac{1}{\text{Settling Time}}$$

$$= \frac{10^6}{4}$$

$$= 250,000 \text{ times/sec}$$

Multiplexers are available that will handle either analogue or digital data channel signals. Digital multiplexers are also referred to as **data selectors** and are available in i.c. form.

4-To-1 Line Digital Multiplexer

The logic diagram of Fig. 2.64 shows an arrangement for multiplexing 4 digital data channels into a commoned output. To select up to 4 channels only a 2-bit address is required which is applied to the channel address lines A and B. For example, with the **enable** line LOW and with a channel address of A = 0, B = 0 the upper AND gate will be enabled, and data applied to the D_o input of the multiplexer will appear at the output of the OR gate. The channel address may be obtained from a counter or from a programme sequence controller. By applying a strobe pulse (active LOW) to the enable line, the switching may be effected at a particular time instant.

When the enable line is HIGH the multiplexer is disabled and this feature permits the expansion of the number of channels by using multiplexer devices together as illustrated in Fig. 2.65. Data selector/multiplexers are

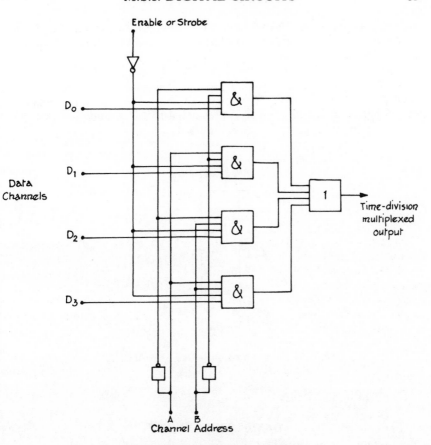

Fig. 2.64 4-to-1 line digital multiplexer.

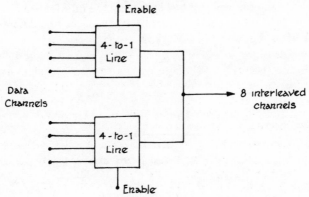

Fig. 2.65 Use of enable line to permit expansion when 4-to-1 line multiplexers are used together.

commonly available for 16-to-1 line, 8-to-1 line, 4-to-1 line and 2-to-1 line applications. All of the essential buffering and channel address decoding is included in the i.c. package.

Pin-out Diagram

The pin-out diagram of the SN74ALS352 data selector/multiplexer is given in Fig. 2.66. This i.c. incorporates two 4-to-1 line multiplexers in the i.c. package with separate strobing inputs.

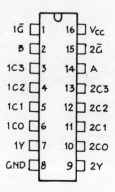

Fig. 2.66 Pin-out diagram of the SN74ALS352.

DEMULTIPLEXERS

When data is transmitted or conveyed using time-division techniques it has to be separated out into its various channels at the receiver and a demultiplexer may be used for this purpose. It performs the opposite function to the multiplexer by separating the interleaved data signals into n channels at its output in the correct sequence, see Fig. 2.67 which shows the basic principle.

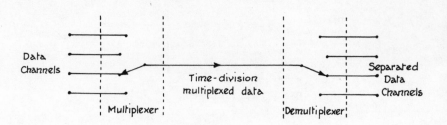

Fig. 2.67 Demultiplexer principle.

As illustrated, the demultiplexer connects the common time-division multiplexed data at its input into one of a number of outputs and if the connection is made for the time interval assigned to individual channel data, separation may be achieved. Not only must the demultiplexer switch make contact for the required channel data period but also the multiplexer and demultiplexer switches should be in synchronism with one another so that channel 1 data applied at the multiplexer input appears at the channel 1 output of the demultiplexer. Thus in a data transmission system some form of 'synchronising' signal should be conveyed along with the data. In a digital control system, *e.g.* industrial process control, the synchronising signals may be provided by a computer.

1-To-4 Line Demultiplexer

The logic circuit of a digital demultiplexer is shown in Fig. 2.68. As is common with many of the commercially available demultiplexers, this arrangement will also operate as a decoder. When used as a demultiplexer, the time-division multiplexed data is applied to the data 1 input and the binary coded channel address is applied to the 'select' inputs A and B. A

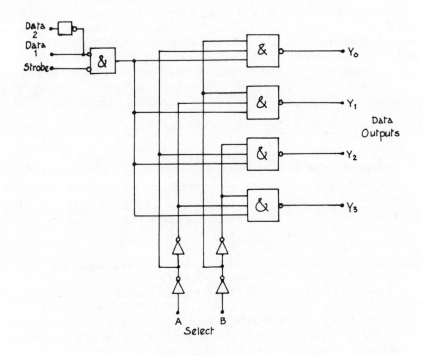

Fig. 2.68 1-to-4 line demultiplexer.

truth table showing the operation when used as a 1-to-4 line demultiplexer is given in Table 2.10.

| Address | | | | Outputs | | | |
A	B	Data 1	Strobe	Y_0	Y_1	Y_2	Y_3
L	L	L	L	L	H	H	H
L	H	L	L	H	L	H	H
H	L	L	L	H	H	L	H
H	H	L	L	H	H	H	L

Table 2.10 Truth table showing operation as a 1-to-4 line demultiplexer

It will be seen that if the data 1 input is in the LOW state, then when a strobe pulse (active LOW) is applied one of the output lines goes to the LOW state, *i.e.* follows the data, with all other output lines remaining in the HIGH state depending on the address input. Similarly with a constant address and with a HIGH on the data 1 input, the selected output will go HIGH with the remaining outputs staying in the HIGH state. Thus **only one output will follow the data** with the other outputs permanently in the HIGH state. Note that the demultiplexer will only switch when a strobe pulse is applied and the duration of the pulse must embrace the period assigned to individual channel data. A truth table showing the operation of the circuit arrangement when used as a 2-to-4 line decoder is given in Table 2.11.

| Select | | | | Outputs | | | |
A	B	Data 2	Strobe	Y_0	Y_1	Y_2	Y_3
L	L	H	L	L	H	H	H
L	H	H	L	H	L	H	H
H	L	H	L	H	H	L	H
H	H	H	L	H	H	H	L

Table 2.11 Truth table showing operation as a 2-to-4 line decoder

The binary signal to be decoded is now applied to the Select inputs A and B and the Data 2 input is held permanently in the HIGH state. When a strobe pulse is applied, one of the output lines goes to the LOW state thus identifying or decoding the select input, with all other output lines remaining in the HIGH state.

```
        1Y2 ⌷ 1        20 ⌷ Vcc
        1Y1 ⌷ 2        19 ⌷ 1Y3
        1Y0 ⌷ 3        18 ⌷ 1B
        1AL ⌷ 4        17 ⌷ 1A
        1OE ⌷ 5        16 ⌷ 1C̄
         2A ⌷ 6        15 ⌷ 2C̄
         2B ⌷ 7        14 ⌷ 2OE
        2Y3 ⌷ 8        13 ⌷ 2AL
        2Y2 ⌷ 9        12 ⌷ 2Y0
        GND ⌷ 10       11 ⌷ 2Y1
```

Fig. 2.69 Pin-out diagram of SN74ALS539.

Pin-Out Diagram

Fig. 2.69 shows the pin-out diagram for the SN74ALS539 dual 2-4 line decoder/demultiplexer with 3-state outputs. This i.c. contains 2 independent decoders each of which accepts 2 address input signals A and B and decodes them to select 1 of 4 mutually exclusive outputs $Y_0 - Y_3$. If the polarity control input (AL) is HIGH, the outputs are active LOW; if AL is LOW the outputs are active HIGH. An active LOW input enable (Ḡ) is available for data demultiplexing and data is routed to the selected output in non-inverted or inverted form. A HIGH on the output enable (OE) forces the 3-state outputs to the high impedance state.

BUFFERS

A buffer amplifier is a circuit which transfers a signal from a sensitive circuit of high output impedance to a low impedance load, see Fig. 2.71. A buffer is essentially a power amplifier that is characterised by a high input impedance so that it presents a light load to the sensitive circuit and a low output impedance so that it can drive heavy loads with comparative ease.

Common examples of buffers or matching circuits include the emitter-follower, source-follower and OP-AMP voltage-follower all of which offer near unity gain. The buffer stages used in digital electronics may be

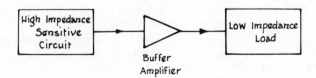

Buffer
Amplifier

Fig. 2.70 Buffer amplifier.

non-inverting, inverting or tri-state and normally provide a voltage gain in excess of unity. Some common uses of buffers are:

(1) To Increase the Fan-Out of a Logic Gate

Suppose that the AND gate of Fig. 2.71 has a fan-out of 10. It could therefore be used to feed 9 loads from output F and the single buffer load.

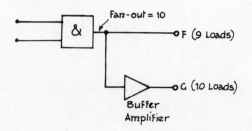

Fig. 2.71 Use of buffer to increase fan-out.

Because the buffer is capable of high current drive from its output, it may be used to drive, say, 10 loads thus enabling 19 loads to be driven (9 from F and 10 from G).

(2) Altering the Logic Level at Input or Output of a Logic Gate

The inverting buffer may be used to alter the logic level at the output of a logic gate as in Fig. 2.72(a) or at the input of a logic gate as in Fig. 2.72(b). In this application the inverting buffer is used as a NOT gate.

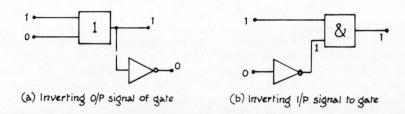

(a) Inverting O/P signal of gate   (b) Inverting I/P signal to gate

Fig. 2.72 Use of buffer to alter logic level.

(3) Buffering Signals to and From a Memory

Tri-state buffers are frequently used to buffer signals to and from a memory array which utilises a common input/output data bus, see Fig. 2.73. When data is being written into the memory the input buffer is enabled and the output buffer is disabled (to prevent the data recirculating). To read from the memory, the input buffer is disabled and the output buffer enabled.

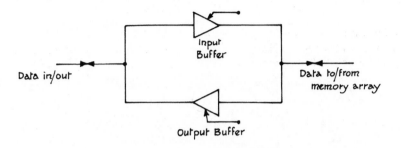

Fig. 2.73 Use of tri-state buffers.

(4) Driving a Data Bus

In some digital systems a common data bus is frequently used to convey signals between the various devices connected to it. Tri-state buffers may be used to avoid conflict on the data bus as illustrated in Fig. 2.74. When the buffers are enabled, they drive the data bus with the logic signals applied at their inputs. In the disabled mode, the buffers will neither drive nor load the data bus as they will be in the high impedance state; each buffer output will then assume the voltage level on its data line.

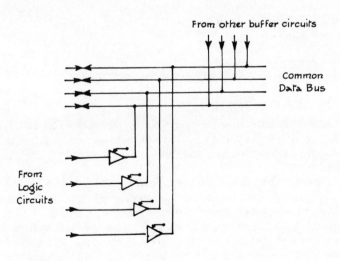

Fig. 2.74 Use of buffers for driving a common data bus.

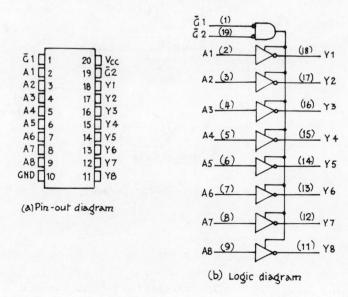

Fig. 2.75 SN54ALS540 octal buffer and line drive.

Pin-Out Diagram

An example of a MSI buffer package is given in Fig. 2.75 for the SN54ALS540. This i.c. package contains 8 buffer stages (inverting types) with tri-state output. The tri-state control is provided by a 2-input NOR gate such that if either G1 or G2 is HIGH all eight Y outputs are in the high impedance state.

AOI AND EX-OR GATES

AND-OR-INVERT (AOI) Gates

A standard combinational logic gate is the AND-OR-INVERT gate which is available in TTL and CMOS. AOI gates are often described as **wide** and the logic diagram for the 7451 dual 2-wide 2-input AOI gate is given in Fig. 2.76.

The upper combinational gate will perform the function $Y = \overline{AB + CD}$ whilst the lower combinational gate will perform the function $X = \overline{EFG + HIJ}$. The AOI gate is a flexible device for if either the inputs A and B or C and D are held permanently LOW, then the gate will perform the function $Y = \overline{AB}$ or $Y = \overline{CD}$. Similarly if E,F and G or H,I and J are held permanently LOW the lower combinational gate will perform the function $X = \overline{EFG}$ or $X = \overline{HIJ}$. Also, if inputs B and C are held permanently HIGH, the upper combinational gate will perform the function $Y = \overline{A + D}$.

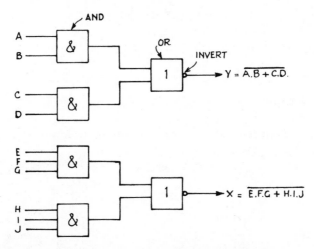

Fig. 2.76 Logic diagram of 7451 dual 2-wide 2-input AOI gate.

Exclusive-OR Gates

An exclusive-OR gate is a 2-input gate whose output assumes the logic 1 state if 1 and only 1 input assumes the logic 1 state, *i.e.* if the input states are different. The logic diagram and truth table for the EX-OR gate are given in Fig. 2.77. Its Boolean expression is given by $F = A\bar{B} + \bar{A}B$ but is sometimes written as $F = A \oplus B$.

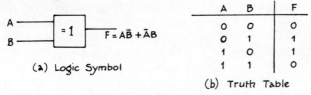

A	B	F
0	0	0
0	1	1
1	0	1
1	1	0

(a) Logic Symbol   (b) Truth Table

Fig. 2.77 Exclusive—OR gate.

The logic diagram of Fig. 2.78 shows how the exclusive-OR function may be implemented using a mixture of OR and AND gates. Exclusive-OR elements are used in the arithmetic section of a computer to check for the inequality of bits, *i.e.* if bit A is not equal to bit B then an output is obtained

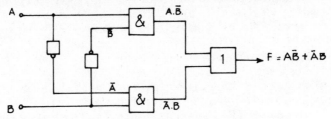

Fig. 2.78 Use of AND and OR gates to produce an EX–OR gate.

whereas if bit A is equal to bit B no output is obtained. An exclusive-OR may also be used as a **controlled inverter** when one of the inputs is used as a strobe. For example, if A is the logic input and a strobe pulse (S) is applied to input B, then $F = \bar{A}$ when S is HIGH and $F = A$ when S is LOW.

Pin-Out Diagram

The pin-out and logic symbol diagrams for the SN74ALS86 quadruple 2-input Exclusive-OR gate package are given in Fig. 2.79.

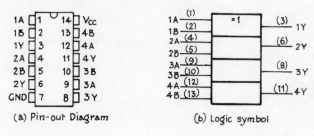

(a) Pin-out Diagram   (b) Logic symbol

Fig. 2.79 SN74ALS86 quadruple 2-input EX–OR gate.

SCHMITT TRIGGERS

A Schmitt trigger is a level sensitive circuit that can have only one of two possible output states. It changes state very rapidly when specific trip points are reached and its main uses include:
(a)   Reshaping of pulses with long rise and fall times.
(b)   Squaring sine wave signals.
(c)   Level detection.
Because of its ability to reshape pulses and eliminate noise it is found as a standard logic gate in most i.c. families.

Basic Operation

A discrete circuit using transistors together with waveforms illustrating the operation are given in Fig. 2.80. When the input to TR1 is zero, TR2 is biassed 'on' via R2 and R3 from TR1 collector. The current in TR2 produces a p.d. across R4 which holds TR1 in the 'off' state. In this state the output voltage from TR2 collector is low. However, the circuit values are usually chosen so that when TR2 is 'on' it is not saturated thus permitting a faster switching speed.

When the input voltage is increased so that it becomes practically equal to the voltage on TR2 base, i.e. it equals the p.d. across R4 plus the forward bias required for TR1 base-emitter junction, TR1 commences to conduct. The resultant fall in TR1 collector voltage causes a fall in TR2 base voltage

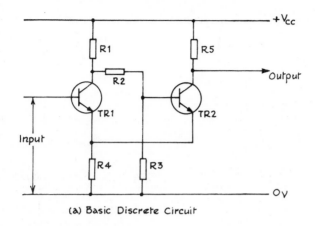

(a) Basic Discrete Circuit

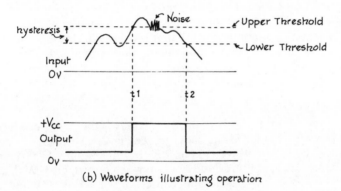

(b) Waveforms illustrating operation

Fig. 2.80 Schmitt trigger operation.

and thus a reduction in TR2 current. As the current in TR2 reduces, the current in TR1 increases which results in a further fall of TR1 collector voltage and TR2 base voltage. This regenerative action results in TR1 rapidly switching 'on' and TR2 rapidly switching 'off'. All of this occurs at instant t_1 when the input reaches the **upper threshold level**. The output from TR2 collector is now in the high voltage state.

This circuit condition persists until the input voltage falls below a lower level, the **lower threshold** when TR1 rapidly switches 'off' and TR2 rapidly switches 'on'. The circuit thus possesses 'hysteresis' and the reason for this is that when TR2 switches 'off', the voltage on its base falls; thus to switch TR1 'off' the input voltage must fall just below TR2 base voltage. This occurs at instant t_2 when the output voltage reverts to the low state.

It will be noted from Fig.2.80(b) that noise present on the input and appearing above the lower threshold is eliminated at the output. Two further

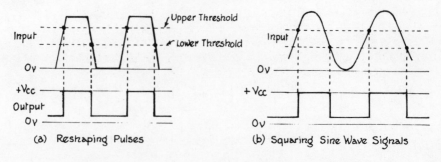

Fig. 2.81 Waveforms illustrating uses of Schmitt trigger.

uses of the Schmitt trigger are illustrated in Fig. 2.81. Fig. 2.81(a) shows how the circuit may be used to reshape pulses which have long rise and fall times; the output pulses have very fast rise and fall times (propagation delay of the order of 16ns). Fig. 2.80(b) shows how the circuit may be used to 'square' a sine wave signal; variations of the input outside the threshold levels have little effect on the output and a good square wave is obtained as the switching is rapid.

Schmitt Trigger I.C.

A common Schmitt trigger in the TTL family is the 7414 i.c. which has 6 Schmitt triggers included in one package, see Fig. 2.82(b). Note the negation sign in the circuit symbol given in Fig. 2.82(b); the output is HIGH when the input is below the lower threshold (inverting Schmitt trigger). With a supply voltage of 5V, the 7414 has an upper threshold of about 1·7V and a lower threshold of about 0·9V thus giving a voltage hysteresis of 0·8V. The propagation delay of each trigger is typically 15ns.

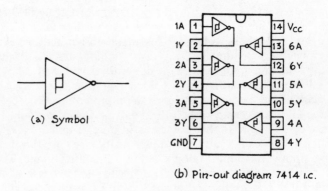

(a) Symbol

(b) Pin-out diagram 7414 i.c.

Fig. 2.82 HEX Schmitt trigger I.C.

Another common Trigger in the TTL range is the 7413 which is a dual NAND Schmitt trigger having 4-inputs to each gate. The circuit symbol is given in Fig. 2.83. A NAND Schmitt is essentially a NAND gate followed by a Schmitt trigger. The input to the trigger will be in the HIGH state only when all of the inputs to the NAND gate are in the LOW state.

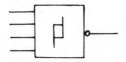

Fig. 2.83 NAND Schmitt trigger.

Schmitt trigger devices are also available in CMOS such as the 4584 (Hex inverting Schmitt) and the 4093 (Quad 2-input NAND Schmitt). These devices have an upper threshold of 2·9V and a lower threshold of 1·9V giving an hysteresis of 1·0V with a 5V supply. A circuit diagram showing the use of a NAND Schmitt trigger as a sine-to-square wave converter is given in Fig. 2.84. The resistors R1 and R2 are used to set the excursions of the input signal midway between the upper and lower threshold levels in order to obtain a symmetrical output.

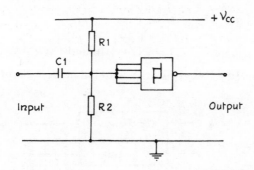

Fig. 2.84 Sine wave-to-square wave converter.

A Schmitt trigger such as the SN7413 makes an excellent astable multivibrator with an operating frequency over the range of about 1Hz to 1MHz. A basic circuit is given in Fig. 2.85 and the operation is as follows.

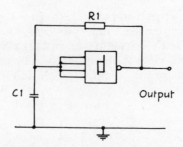

Fig. 2.85 Schmitt trigger astable multivibrator.

Suppose that initially C1 is uncharged thus the input to the NAND Schmitt trigger is LOW and the output is HIGH. C1 will now charge via R1 towards the HIGH voltage at the output. When the voltage across C1 reaches the upper threshold of about 1·7V, the output rapidly switches to the LOW state. C1 now discharges via R1 and the voltage across the capacitor commences to fall. When the voltage has fallen to about 0·8V (the lower threshold) the output reverts to the HIGH state once more. The process of alternate charging and discharging of C1 continues at a rate determined by the time constant of C1, R1.

BINARY ADDERS

A digital computer or calculator must be able to add binary numbers according to the following rules:

$$
\begin{array}{ccl}
A & B & SUM \\
0 + 0 & = & 0 \\
0 + 1 & = & 1 \\
1 + 0 & = & 1 \\
1 + 1 & = & 0 \text{ and CARY 1}
\end{array}
$$

This may be carried out using a combinational logic circuit, see Fig. 2.86.

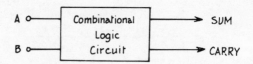

Fig. 2.86 Addition of binary numbers.

Inspection of the rules shows that the SUM column requires the use of the Exclusive-OR function, thus the required logic circuit is as shown in Fig. 2.87. This is known as a **half-adder**.

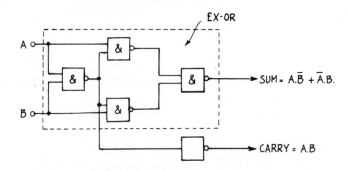

Fig. 2.87 Half-adder logic circuit.

Full-Adder

In the addition process, an electronic adder must be capable of adding three binary digits: digit A, digit B and the carry digit from the previous column according to the rules:

A	B	Carry In	SUM	CARRY OUT
0	0	0	0	0
0	0	1	1	0
0	1	0	1	0
0	1	1	0	1
1	0	0	1	0
1	0	1	0	1
1	1	0	0	1
1	1	1	1	1

Two half-adders are required to perform this process and the combinational logic circuit becomes a full-adder, see Fig. 2.88.

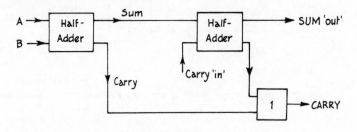

(a)   Full - Adder Schematic

Fig. 2.88 Full adder.

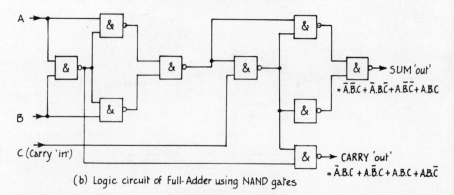

(b) Logic circuit of Full-Adder using NAND gates

Fig. 2.88(b) Full adder.

Serial Adder

Two multi-digit binary numbers may be added serially, *i.e.* one column at a time commencing with the column for the least significant digits and carrying over any carry digit to the next column by employing just one

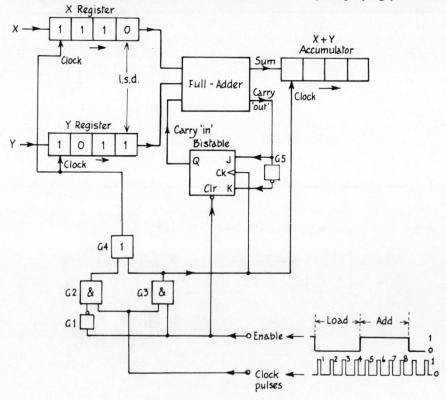

Fig. 2.89 Serial adder (Basic idea).

full-adder. The basic idea is illustrated in Fig. 2.89 where some sup-plementary units are also included. Two data shift registers (X and Y registers) are needed to hold the two binary numbers (assumed to be 4-digit) which are to be added together. An accumulator (shift register) is required to hold the result of the binary addition and a J-K bistable store to hold the carry digit for addition in the next column. Also, a control circuit consisting of gates G1–G4 is needed.

When the enable input first goes LOW, the bistable is cleared and G2 is enabled allowing clock pulses 1–4 to pass through G2 and G4 to clock the binary digits serially into the X and Y registers. Assume that after these four clock pulses the binary numbers shown have been clocked into the registers and that the X and Y inputs are returned to logic 0.

Following clock pulse 4 when the enable line goes HIGH, the clear is removed from the bistable and G3 is enabled allowing clock pulses to be fed to the input registers via G3 and G4 and to the bistable and accumulator via G3.

The diagrams of Fig. 2.90 illustrate the sequence of events when the enable line is taken HIGH. Fig. 2.90(a) shows the logic state at the end of the loading period when the Q output of the bistable is at logic 0 after clearing of the bistable. It will be seen that the sum of the full-adder inputs is logic 1 and the C_o is logic 0.

On the following clock pulse (number 5), the numbers in the X and Y registers are shifted one place to the right, the sum digit of (a) is transferred to the accumulator and the C_o digit of (a) is clocked into the Q output of the bistable. Thus at the end of clock pulse 5, the logic state will be as in Fig. 2.90(b).

During clock pulses 6, 7 and 8 this process is repeated with the sum digit from the **previous** operation being transferred to the accumulator and the C_o digit from the **previous** operation being stored in the bistable output.

At the end of clock pulse 8, the sum is stored in the accumulator with the carry out digit from the most significant column addition stored in the Q output of the bistable.

Parallel Adder

In serial addition, presenting each pair of digits in a timed sequence to the full-adder is a relatively slow process compared with parallel addition where the answer is produced almost instantaneously.

Figure 2.91 shows the basic idea of a 4-bit parallel adder such as the SN7483. This is capable of adding together two 4-bit binary numbers but requires four full-adders as shown.

The logic states given on the diagram illustrate the operation when adding the two binary numbers P and Q (0101 + 1110) where P1 and Q1 are the least significant digits. The carry-in(C_i) terminal of the l.s.d. full-adder is permanently hard-wired to logic 0.

Considering the operation in pairs of digits; P1 and Q1 are added in FA1, producing a sum of logic 1 and a C_o of logic 0. In FA2 the digits P2 and Q2 are

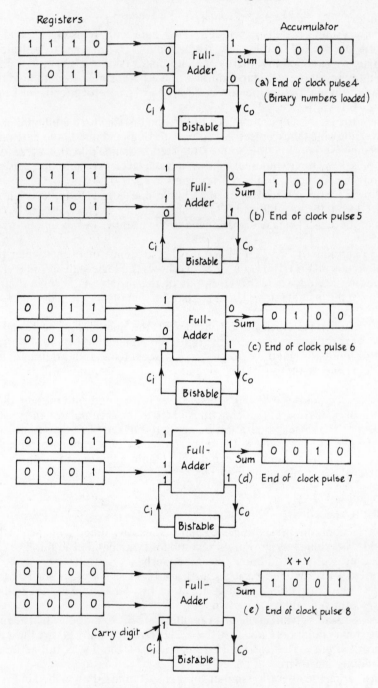

Fig. 2.90 Sequence of events during serial addition.

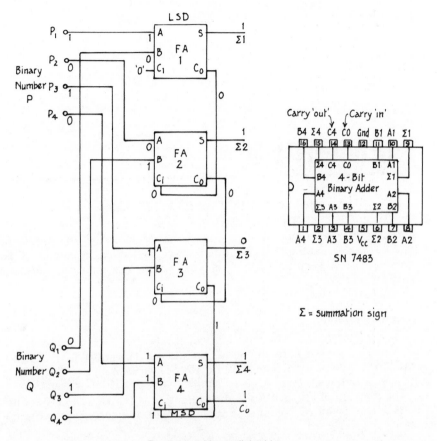

Fig. 2.91 4-bit parallel adder.

added to the C_i producing a sum of logic 1 and a C_o of logic 0. Full-adder FA3 adds together P3, Q3 and the C_i resulting in a sum of logic 0 and a C_o of logic 1. Finally, FA4 adds together P4, Q4 and the C_i digits to produce a sum of logic 1 and a C_o of logic 1.

Two 4-bit adders may be used together to produce an 8-bit adder by wiring the C_o of the m.s.d. F.A. of one 4-bit device to the C_i of the l.s.d. F.A. of the other 4-bit device.

CHAPTER 3

MEMORIES

SEMICONDUCTOR RAM MEMORY

A RAM OR READ-WRITE memory is a memory store where data can be stored or retrieved randomly (Random Access Memory). A semiconductor type RAM is a **voltatile** store, *i.e.* when power is removed the content of the memory is lost; when the memory is powered up once again the content is 'garbage'.

Store Organisation

Each 'bit' of data is stored in an unique location within the memory. The capacity of a store is normally quoted in **kilobits**. The prefix 'kilo' does not stand for 1000 as is usual but for 2^{10} or 1024. Thus 30 kilobits = 30 K = 30 × 1024 = 30720 bits.

The diagram of Fig. 3.1 shows the organisation of a 1K store (1024 bits) with 32 rows and 32 columns. Each of the 1024 squares represents the

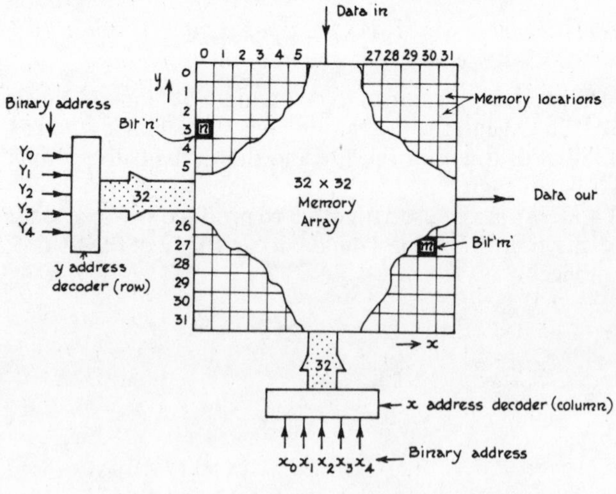

Fig. 3.1 Standard 1k RAM.

location for 1-bit of information (a logic 1 or logic 0). Any location may be specified by its column and row address, *e.g.* bit 'n' may be specified as x_0/y_3 and bit 'm' by x_{30}/y_{27}. With a semiconductor type RAM the memory locations are usually formed by flip-flops fabricated in i.c. form using either Bipolar or CMOS technology. A 'square' matrix is normally used as this results in the least number of connecting lines to be made to the memory array.

Adressing the Memory

To place data in a memory location (write) or withdraw data (read) each location must be addressed and usually the 'address' is the binary code. The 32 rows and 32 columns of the standard 1K memory may each be specified by a 5-bit binary code ($2^5 = 32$) giving 0–31. To decode the 5-bit binary address a 5 line-to-32 line binary-to-decimal decoder is required for row and column addressing. The locations may be addressed in strict sequence commencing with x_0y_0 proceeding to x_1y_0, x_2y_0, x_3y_0 up to $x_{31}y_0$ then on to the next row x_0y_1, x_1y_1, x_2y_1 up to $x_{31}y_1$ and so on until the last location $x_{31}y_{31}$ has been addressed.

During the 'write' operation as each location is addressed a single bit (logic 0 or 1) from the 'data in' line is placed in that location. During the 'read' operation as each location is addressed the stored bit will appear on the 'data out' line, one bit at a time. In practice it does not matter in what order the bits are written into the memory, as long as they are read out from the memory in the same order.

Parallel Operation

When a large bit storage is required, standard 1K memories may be used arranged in planes as in Fig. 3.2. This arrangement is often used to permit the simultaneous storage and retrieval of n-bit 'words'. For example a 7-bit word would require 7 planes thereby permitting parallel addressing of the seven 1K RAMS. Consider the storage of a 7-bit word. Bit 1 may be stored in, say, location x_3y_3 in plane 1, bit 2 stored at the same location x_3y_3 in plane 2, bit 3 stored at x_3y_3 in plane 3 and so on. The location x_3y_3 in each plane may be addressed simultaneously thereby writing into or reading from the memory a complete 7-bit word in a single address operation. This speeds up the whole process of writing and reading.

A common display format for a visual display unit uses 24 rows of text where each row is capable of holding up to 40 characters (alphanumerics). Since each character is often represented by a 7-bit code, a suitable memory capacity would therefore be $40 \times 24 \times 7$ bits = 6720 bits. The seven 1K memories arranged in planes would meet this requirement and a practical arrangement is shown in Fig. 3.3

The use of seven 1K bit organised RAMS results in an exact word length but there will be some 448 bits of spare storage space. The read/write operation is under the control of the R/$\overline{\text{W}}$ input line. When a LOW is applied

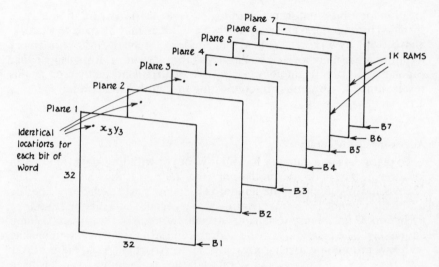

Fig. 3.2 Parallel operation (7 × 1k RAM).

to this line, the memory is placed in the 'write' mode; a HIGH will place it in the 'read' mode. The chip select ($\overline{CS}$) line may be used to inhibit the addressing of the memory by placing a HIGH on this input. It is normally held LOW during the 'read' and 'write' cycles.

It will be noted that the address inputs, chip select and read/write control input for each of the 7 memory i.cs. are connected so that they appear as a single memory i.c. These particular 1K RAMS use separate data-in and

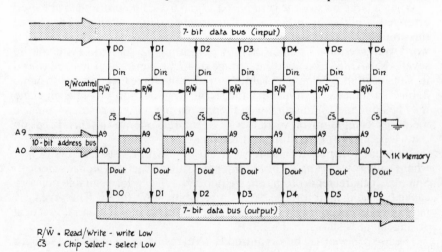

$R/\overline{W}$ = Read/Write - write Low
$\overline{CS}$ = Chip Select - select Low

Fig. 3.3 Use of 7 1k RAMs for storing a screen full of data in a V.D.U.

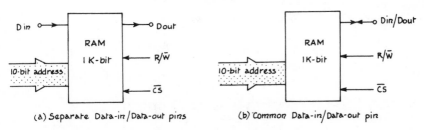

(a) Separate Data-in/Data-out pins   (b) Common Data-in/Data-out pin

Fig. 3.4 Bit organised RAM.

data-out pins but sometimes a common pin is used for data-in/data-out, see Fig. 3.4 for variation in pin connections. A common data-in/data-out pin is used with systems employing a single data bus.

Word Organised RAM

Some RAMS are designed to create a word organised structure. With such a memory, a complete word of, say, 4-bits is stored in the memory array for each memory address. Note that each bit of the word must have its own memory 'cell', all memory cells being accessed simultaneously when the address is applied.

In a memory organised as a 1K 4-bit word RAM, see Fig. 3.5, there will be 1024×4, *i.e.* 4K-bits of storage capacity. As each word is associated with a single address, a 10-bit address will specify the 1024 words.

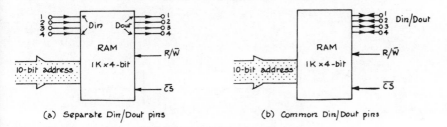

(a) Separate Din/Dout pins   (b) Common Din/Dout pins

Fig. 3.5 Word organised RAM.

Static and Dynamic RAM cells

The memory cells in a semiconductor RAM are often classified as 'static' or 'dynamic'. With a static RAM the information that is stored is retained, *i.e.* is static as long as the power supply to the memory is kept 'on'. However with a dynamic RAM, information is stored in the form of a charge on a capacitor which has to be periodically refreshed because of charge leakage.

The basic memory cell in a static RAM consists of a flip-flop; a separate flip-flop is required for each bit to be stored. Each flip-flop has to be addressed using row and column addressing as illustrated in Fig. 3.6(a). A pair of read/write lines is made common to all cells or flip-flops in the matrix so that data may be written into or read from any cell in the memory matrix.

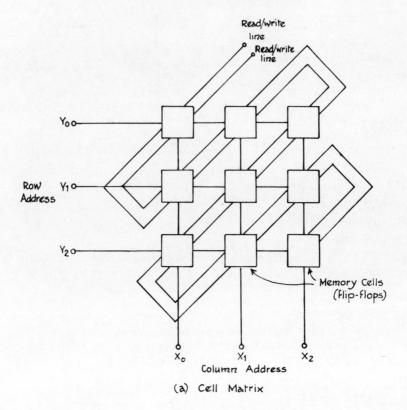

(a) Cell Matrix

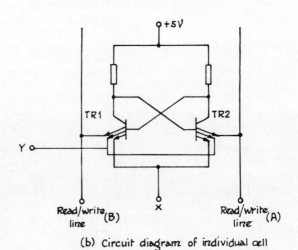

(b) Circuit diagram of individual cell

Fig. 3.6 Static RAM based on bipolar technology.

A circuit diagram of an individual cell based on bipolar technology is given in Fig. 3.6(b). To address a particular cell, the X and Y address lines unique to that cell are taken HIGH. In the non-addressed cells one or both of the X/Y address lines will be LOW.

To write data into a cell the X and Y address lines must be taken to the HIGH state and the data (1 or 0) and its complement applied to the read/write. Suppose that logic 1 (HIGH) is applied to the read/write line B and a logic 0 (LOW) to the read/write line A. Transistor TR1 connected to the HIGH read/write line will not be able to conduct but TR2 connected to the LOW read/write line will conduct. In this state with TR1 'off' and TR2 'on' the flip-flop is storing, say, a logic 1. At the end of the write cycle, the flip-flop will remain in this state since one or both of its X and Y address lines will be taken LOW thereby maintaining TR2 'on' and TR1 'off'. With the logic conditions reversed on the read/write lines, then TR1 would be 'on' and TR2 'off' thus storing a logic 0.

To read the cell content the X and Y lines must be taken HIGH which causes current in the 'on' transistor to be diverted into one of the read/write lines. Assuming that a logic 1 has been stored then current would flow in the read/write line A. A sense amplifier connected to both of the read/write lines will detect the current in line A and output a logic 1. Had a logic 0 been stored, the sense amplifier would have detected the current flow in line B and outputted a logic 0. When the contents of a cell is read, the information stored is not lost-'non-destructive read-out'.

A static RAM cell based on CMOS technology is given in Fig. 3.7. The

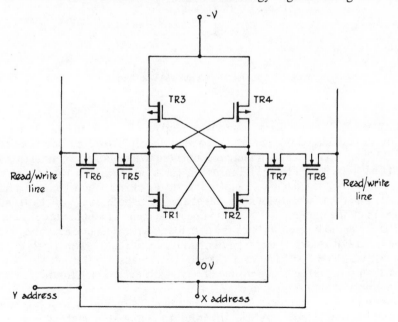

Fig. 3.7 CMOS static RAM cell.

n-channel MOSFETS TR1 and TR2 form the flip-flop with the p-channel devices TR3 and TR4 serving as active loads. The principle of operation is similar to that of the bipolar cell with addressing applied via TR5, TR6 and TR7, TR8 which essentially form AND gates between the read/write lines and the memory cell. The read/write lines are only connected to the memory cell when a negative potential is applied simultaneously to the X and Y address lines. CMOS static RAMS have a lower power dissipation than the bipolar RAMS in the TTL range but have a longer access time. Static RAMS are also available in ECL and I^2L with ECL offering the fastest access time of all the logic families.

The circuit diagram of a dynamic random access memory (DRAM) storage cell using 3 MOS transistors is shown in Fig. 3.8. This type of memory cell relies for its action on temporary storage of charge in a

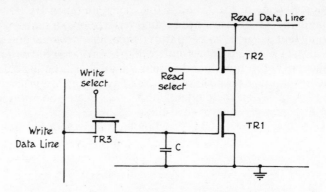

Fig. 3.8 3-transistor dynamic RAM cell (dram).

capacitor (C). When a 'write' pulse is applied to TR3 gate, the data (1 or 0) on the write data line is stored in C. To read the cell a 'read' pulse is applied to TR2 gate and the read data line is connected to a negative potential (logic 1). If C stores a logic 1 then TR1 turns 'on' (also TR2 turns 'on') and the read data line is discharged to 0V (logic 0). If C stores a logic 0 then TR1 and TR2 are 'off' and the read data line remains at a negative potential (logic 1). It will be seen that the data on the read data line is the complement of the cell data. This is corrected by feeding back the data to the write data line after the read cycle. A disadvantage of this type of memory cell is that C, which is the gate capacitance of TR1, suffers from leakage. This means that the data stored in the cell must be 'refreshed' periodically (typically every 2ms); for this reason the memory is called 'dynamic'.

Dynamic RAMS have a higher packing density and a lower power dissipation than static RAMS. In order to obtain the highest possible packing density a single transistor dynamic RAM cell was developed, see

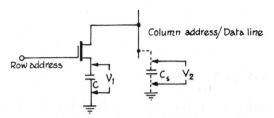

Fig. 3.9 Single transistor dynamic RAM cell.

Fig. 3.9. Here the column address also serves as the data-in/out line for all cells in each column. When row and column addresses are applied to select a particular cell, the voltage across C is transferred to the data line during 'read' or a voltage from the data line is applied to C during 'write'. One design problem with these cells is to obtain a sufficiently large read-out voltage when C is in the HIGH voltage state. This difficulty occurs because when a particular cell is selected for readng, C is placed in parallel with C_S (the capacitance of the data line). Since $C_S \gg C$, the read-out voltage V_2 is very much less than the cell voltage V_1. It is therfore necessary to regenerate the stored information after every read operation to its original level V_1. Additionally, due to charge leakage from C, it must be periodically refreshed.

To detect the state of any cell, 'sense amplifiers' based on flip-flop circuits are employed as illustrated in Fig. 3.10, which shows the basic idea for a single-transistor dynamic RAM array; there is one sense amplifier for each column of cells. The sense amplifiers are responsible for regenerating the output voltage of the cells to a value that is comparable with the voltage across the storage capacitors. Additionally the amplifiers carry out the 'refreshing' action of the storage capacitors.

Fig. 3.10 shows the operation when 'reading' the data from storage capacitor C22 (row 2, column 2). During 'read', TR22 is turned 'on' by the line 2 output of the row address decoder; transistors in all other rows being turned 'off'. The line 2 output of the column address decoder closes the transmission gates G5 and G6. With a HIGH applied to the read/write control line, transmission gate G1 will be open and G2 closed. The column 2 sense amplifier senses and regenerates the stored voltage from C22 and applies it via G2 to the data output line.

During the reading of row 2, column 2 location, other transistors in row 2 will be turned 'on' by the line 2 output of the row address decoder. For example, TR23 will be 'on' thereby permitting the charge on C23 to be refreshed by the special action performed by the column 3 sense amplifier. This does not affect the data output as G4 is open.

A similar action takes place during the 'write' operation. Consider writing into storage location row 2, column 2. Transmission gate G1 is now closed (G2 open) and the data from the data-in line is applied to the column 2 sense amplifier. The amplifier latches on to the incoming data and applies it to storage capacitor C22 via TR22 which is 'on'.

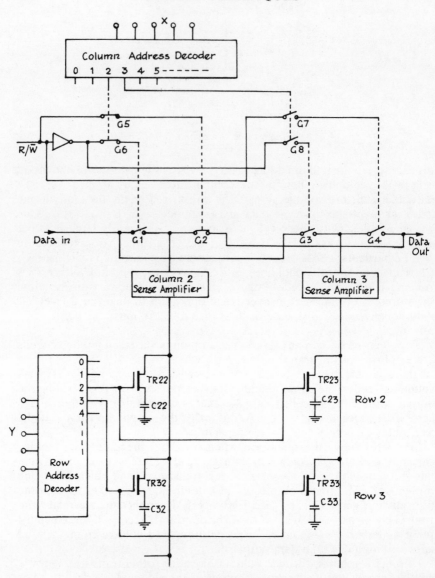

Fig. 3.10 Part of array of single-transistor dynamic RAM cells.

READ ONLY MEMORY (ROM)

With this type of memory information can only be 'read' from the memory. Once a ROM has been produced, information cannot be written into it. After a ROM has been programmed the data is permanently stored and remains when the power is switched 'off', hence a ROM is a **non-volatile** store. The data stored in **hardware** form in a ROM is referred to as **firmware**.

Principle of ROMs

ROMs are essentially non-volatile, high speed, high density, random access storage matrices. The data is stored as a pattern of HIGHs and LOWs (logic 1s and 0s). The memory consists of combinational logic circuitry with 'permanent' connections which determine the stored data rather than sequential flip-flop elements. The term 'random access' means that the access time to the information stored in an addressed location is practically always the same irrespective of the address of the location and the previous location addressed. Although 'random access' applies to a ROM it is not normally included in the name of the memory; it is accepted that the device is random access. Care has to be taken since a ROM is quite different from a RAM (Random Access Memory) which is a read/write memory.

Most modern ROMs are 'word' organised and Fig. 3.11 shows the basic idea. Suppose that the memory matrix has 2048 cells and that the matrix is organised into 256 8-bit words. When an address is applied to the memory matrix, the contents stored in the 8 locations associated with that address will

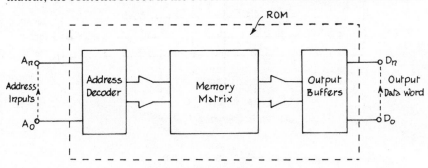

Fig. 3.11 ROM organisation.

be placed on the 8-output lines from the matrix. The matrix output is processed by the output buffers shown, and an 8-bit parallel data word appears on the data outputs of the ROM. Rather than having to supply the ROM with 256 addresses, address decoding is carried out within the ROM. In this example the address decoder would be an 8 to 256 line decoder.

Diode Matrix ROM

Consider a simple 16-bit (4 × 4) ROM as illustrated in Fig. 3.12. The memory is said to be organised in a 4-word, 4-bit configuration. If p-n diodes are used to form the required permanent connections in the memory array, the diode matrix would be arranged in the unprogrammed state as in Fig. 3.13(a). With an unprogrammed matrix, since there is no connection

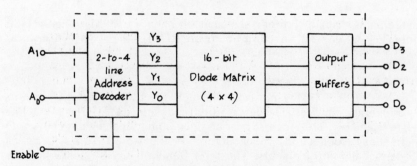

Fig. 3.12 16-bit diode matrix ROM.

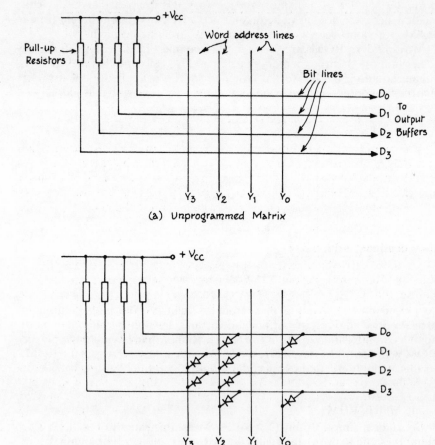

(a) Unprogrammed Matrix

(b) Programmed Matrix

Fig. 3.13 Diode matrix before and after programming.

between the word and bit lines, all of the bits of the output word will be HIGH ($+V_{CC}$) irrespective of the address. The memory is therefore 'blank'.

Bits of a word are programmed LOW by placing a diode at the intersection of a bit line and word line. A particular word is accessed by making the appropriate address line LOW (0V). Note that a LOW on a word address line will cause any connected diodes to conduct hard thus the bit line will assume approximately zero potential (logic 0). With a HIGH ($+V_{CC}$) on a word address line, the 'anode' and 'cathode' of a diode will be at the same potential and the bit line assumes $+V_{CC}$ (logic 1). The truth table showing the output words for the arrangement of Fig. 3.13(b) is given in Table 3.1.

Y_0	Y_1	Y_2	Y_3	D_0	D_1	D_2	D_3	
0	1	1	1	0	1	1	0	Stored Word 1
1	0	1	1	1	1	1	1	Stored Word 2
1	1	0	1	0	0	0	0	Stored Word 3
1	1	1	0	1	0	0	1	Stored Word 4

Table 3.1 Truth Table for Diode Matrix of Fig. 3.13(b)

The output buffers ensure that the ROM has normal TTL compatibility and they may be inverting or non-inverting. If tri-state buffers are used, the enable/disable for the ROM will be carried out in the buffers. With many modern ROMSs bipolar or CMOS transistor circuitry replaces the diodes in the matrix but the basic operating principles remain the same.

2-Dimensional Addressing

Consider a ROM matrix holding 4096 bits of data arranged in the common 1024×4-bit configuration. If one-dimensional addressing is employed as considered in the previous ROMs then the connections to and from the matrix would be as in Fig. 3.14. The total number of connections made to the matrix would be $1024 + 4 = 1028$. By using 2-dimensional addressing, the number of connections to the matrix may be significantly reduced as the practical example shown in Fig. 3.15 serves to illustrate.

The 4096-bit ROM is now arranged as a 64×64-bit word matrix having 64 address lines and 64 output data bit lines (4×16). Address inputs 4 to 9 inclusive are used to select any of the 64 stored words. When a word is selected, its 64-bits are supplied in 4 groups of 16-bits to multiplexers. By using 16 to 1 multiplexers the bits of the selected word may be used in 16 different combinations to provide 16 4-bit words at the ROM output. The number of connections required for the matrix has reduced from 1028 to only 128. Address inputs 0 to 3 inclusive provide the address for the multiplexer. From the external point of view the ROM will behave as if it

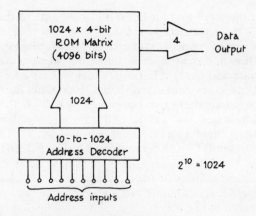

Fig. 3.14 One-dimensional addressing.

were using addressing in one dimension only and as if it were actually a 1024 × 4-bit ROM.

It is common practice to refer to the 6 to 64 address decoder as the row decoder and the multiplexer decoder as the column decoder in keeping with normal matrix terminology. It can be shown that the least number of connections is required for the matrix when the total number of rows equals

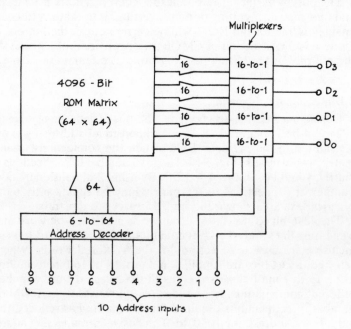

Fig 3.15 2-dimensional addressing.

the total number of columns, *i.e.* the matrix is square. It is not always possible to have a square matrix since the array must have sides which are exact multiples of 2, *i.e.* 2, 4, 8, 16, 32, 64 *etc.* in order to be able to address the matrix. Therefore it follows that the 'nearest' to square configuration is used. For example, consider a memory of 1024 × 8-bits (8192 bits). The nearest to a 'square array' is a 128 × 64-bit array which gives a reduction in connections from 1032 to only 192.

Programmable Read Only Memory (PROM)

This type of ROM is produced so that programming may be carried out after production, often by the purchaser. When the PROM is made, the bits of the memory are either all HIGH or all LOW. Programming causes some of the bit states to be reversed. A common method of producing a PROM is to include in each storage cell a titanium-tungsten link or fuse (Ti-W) and it is this which permits programming of the memory at a later date. When the PROM leaves the production line the memory is 'blank' and since the device is non-committed it can be mass produced. The basic idea is shown in Fig. 3.16 for a simple diode matrix PROM. If any of the word address lines is taken LOW, all of the output bits will be LOW and the memory is blank. Programming of the memory entails the 'blowing' of some of the Ti-W fusible links causing the appropriate bits to reverse to the HIGH state. If a particular bit is to be programmed LOW then the link is left intact.

Once a bit has been programmed HIGH, it can never be changed. Cells remaining LOW can, however, be programmed HIGH at any later time. In general therefore, the programming of a PROM is an irreversible process. Once a PROM has been programmed then it effectively becomes just a ROM.

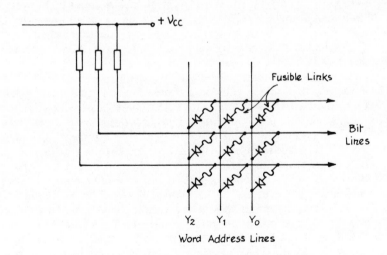

Fig. 3.16 Diode matrix PROM (memory blank).

Eraseable Programmable Read Only Memory (EPROM)

With this type of PROM the programming is not an irreversible process. The memory contents may be erased and the PROM reprogrammed. At the present time it is not known whether there is a limit to the number of times this can be carried out. The EPROM can usually be identified by the 'quartz window' on the top of the device, see Fig. 3.17(a).

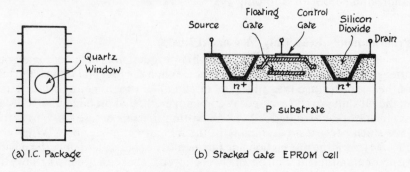

(a) I.C. Package   (b) Stacked Gate EPROM Cell

Fig. 3.17 EPROM.

Programming of a memory cell is achieved by the storage of a charge in a cell location using a 25–50V pulse. Erasure of the EPROM contents is carried out by exposing the memory matrix to short wave ultra-violet light. This is the reason for the 'quartz lid'. The wavelength of the u.v. source is typically 253·7n.m. and the typical integrated u.v. dose for erasure (u.v. intensity × exposure time) is 6 watt/cm^2. Clearly, the time for erasure is variable depending upon the intensity of the u.v. source and the distance between the source and the EPROM. Typical erasure times lie between 10 and 30 minutes. Some EPROMS do exhibit a sensitivity to ambient light. This does not erase them, but they may malfunction when minute photoelectric leakage currents are generated. It is thus prudent to cover the quartz window with some opaque material when the EPROM is operated in an illuminated environment.

The structure of a single cell for a 'stacked-gate' EPROM is given in Fig. 3.17(b). This uses a MOS transistor with a control gate which is used for programming and the 'read' operation. During programming a 25V pulse is applied to the Drain and Control Gate (with the Source and Substrate grounded). This causes some electrons to be transported to the floating gate where they remain more or less idefinitely. When a cell is selected to be read by applying a voltage to the control gate (to enhance the n-channel between source and drain), the presence of the trapped electrons on the floating gates keeps the MOS transistor non-conducting (output logic 0). When a voltage is applied to the control gate of an unprogrammed cell, the n-channel will be enhanced normally and the MOS transistor will conduct (output logic 1). Exposure to u.v. light causes an increase in conductivity of the silicon dioxide allowing the charges on the floating gate to leak away.

This type of memory is particularly useful when developing a system since changes are usually necessary as the development proceeds. The data can simply be erased and the memory reprogrammed. EPROMS are often employed in situations where the data needs to be changed periodically. EPROMS are considerably more expensive than PROMS but this is usually outweighed by the fact that they can be erased and reprogrammed.

Electrically Alterable Read Only Memory (EAROM)

With this type of PROM the contents of the memory matrix can be erased electrically by using high voltages outside the normal operating voltage range and then reprogrammed. This removes the distinct disadvantage of the need for a u.v. source when an EPROM is used. Also, an EAROM requires only about 1 second for erasure compared to 10-30 minutes for the EPROM, thus an EAROM can be used in situations where fast changes in the stored data is a requirement.

The operation of one type of EAROM is very similar in principle to that of the 'stacked-gate' cell described previously using the 'floating gate' arrangement. During programming a positive voltage is applied to the control gate which causes the floating gate to aquire a negative charge which keeps the device 'off'. To erase the contents of the cell a negative voltage is applied to the control gate which causes positive charges to be induced on the floating gate, thereby allowing the device to conduct. Depending upon the storage capacity of an EAROM, erasure can be confined to bytes, blocks of data or individual bits whereas an EPROM must be erased in total.

APPLICATIONS FOR ROMS

Some of the more common applications for ROMs will now be discussed.

Truth Tables

A ROM is essentially a code-conversion unit which translates the code applied to the address decoder into a different code at the ROM output bit lines. In a computer, routine calculations such as square roots, logarithms and trigonometrical functions are sometimes required and if these are repeated often enough it may be more efficient to use a ROM as a 'look-up table' rather than use a software programming routine to perform the calculation. For example it may be required to compute the sine value of any given angle which is applied as an input via the computer keyboard. The arrangement of Fig. 3.18 shows the essential idea of how a ROM may be used to provide the sine value of any whole angle between 0° and 360°. The magnitude of the angle is applied in binary form to the Y address input of the ROM address decoder; a 9-bit binary code would be required to specify angles up to 360°. A 9 to 512 address decoder is capable, of course, of providing 512 addresses but only 360 would be needed in this case. At each address the sine value appropriate to the angle would be programmed into

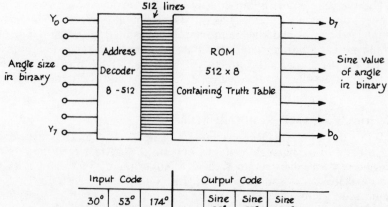

Fig. 3.18 Use of ROM to find the sine of an angle.

Input Code				Output Code		
30°	53°	174°		Sine 30°	Sine 53°	Sine 174°
Y_0 0	1	0	b_7	1	1	0
Y_1 1	0	1	b_6	0	1	0
Y_2 1	1	1	b_5	0	0	0
Y_3 1	0	1	b_4	0	0	1
Y_4 1	1	0	b_3	0	1	1
Y_5 0	1	1	b_2	0	1	0
Y_6 0	0	0	b_1	0	0	1
Y_7 0	0	1	b_0	0	0	0

(Binary Point after b_7 output row)

Sine values programmed into ROM

the unique address in binary form during manufacture, thus creating a table of sine values that are permanently stored in the ROM. When an address is supplied to the ROM, the sine value relating to the angle producing the address will be outputted from the ROM (a few examples are given in the table of Fig. 3.18). The binary coded output may be to whatever accuracy is desired by choice of the ROM word size.

Any calculation for which a truth table can be written can be implemented by a ROM and normally a separate ROM is required for each truth table. Apart from calculations, it may be desired to produce a truth table which represents some logical sequence of signal instructions, *e.g.* signals to operate a traffic light sequencer or to control a washing machine or machine tool. Since these devices require only on/off type signalling to initiate their various actions, control may be implemented by the logic 1s and 0s stored in truth table form in a ROM.

The diagram of Fig. 3.19 illustrates a method for using a ROM as a traffic light sequencer. It is assumed here that the red, amber and green bit line outputs of the ROM are buffered and correctly interfaced with the light sources, also that a logic 1 on an output bit line represents light 'on' and a logic 0 means light 'off'. Suppose that the repetitive 'on' timing sequence for the lights is Green 30 secs, Amber 2 secs, Red 30 secs and Red/Amber 2 secs.

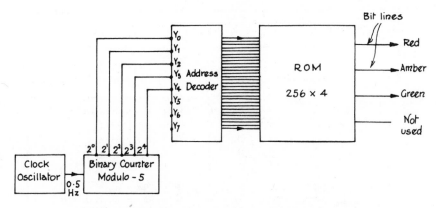

Fig. 3.19 Use of ROM as sequencer for traffic light signals.

It would be convenient here to use a standard timing interval of 2 secs which is provided by the 0·5Hz clock oscillator. The pulse output of the clock oscillator is counted by a modulo-32 binary counter whose output lines provide 32 addresses for the ROM address decoder (only 32 of the available 256 4-bit words will be used). At each address, 3 of the available 4 output bits would be programmed with the logic states as shown in Table 3.2.

Once switched 'on' and pulsed by the clock oscillator the binary counter will continually sweep the addresses of the ROM to provide the 'on' and 'off' signalling for the traffic light display. The 'on' period of the lights may be adjusted by altering the clock oscillator frequency, but if the timing ratio needs to alter the ROM will need reprogramming. During development of such a system an EPROM or EAROM would be used.

A ROM may be used in a similar way to the traffic light sequencer to provide control signals for, say, an automatic washing machine, see Fig. 3.20. The logic control signals representing the 'on' and 'off' sequencing for such items as water inlet valves, drum motor, water heater and water pump *etc.* may be programmed into the ROM in the form of a truth table.

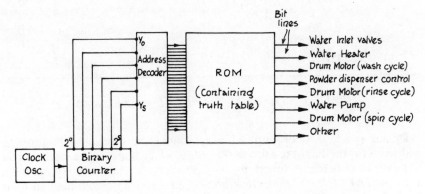

Fig. 3.20 Use of ROM as control source for automatic washing machine.

Clock Pulse No.		Y Address					ROM Truth Table		
		Y_4	Y_3	Y_2	Y_1	Y_0	R	A	G
	0	0	0	0	0	0	0	0	1
	1	0	0	0	0	1	0	0	1
	2	0	0	0	1	0	0	0	1
	3	0	0	0	1	1	0	0	1
	4	0	0	1	0	0	0	0	1
	5	0	0	1	0	1	0	0	1
	6	0	0	1	1	0	0	0	1
	7	0	0	1	1	1	0	0	1
	8	0	1	0	0	0	0	0	1
	9	0	1	0	0	1	0	0	1
	10	0	1	0	1	0	0	0	1
	11	0	1	0	1	1	0	0	1
	12	0	1	1	0	0	0	0	1
	13	0	1	1	0	1	0	0	1
	14	0	1	1	1	0	0	0	1
	15	0	1	1	1	1	0	1	0
	16	1	0	0	0	0	1	0	0
	17	1	0	0	0	1	1	0	0
	18	1	0	0	1	0	1	0	0
	19	1	0	0	1	1	1	0	0
	20	1	0	1	0	0	1	0	0
	21	1	0	1	0	1	1	0	0
	22	1	0	1	1	0	1	0	0
	23	1	0	1	1	1	1	0	0
	24	1	1	0	0	0	1	0	0
	25	1	1	0	0	1	1	0	0
	26	1	1	0	1	0	1	0	0
	27	1	1	0	1	1	1	0	0
	28	1	1	1	0	0	1	0	0
	29	1	1	1	0	1	1	0	0
	30	1	1	1	1	0	1	0	0
	31	1	1	1	1	1	1	1	0
(Counter resets)	32	0	0	0	0	0	0	0	1

Table 3.2 Truth table for traffic light sequencer

During machine operation a binary counter may be used to provide addresses for the ROM to initiate the output of the appropriate logic signals to control the machine functions. The pulses to be counted may again be generated by a free-running clock oscillator using a suitable timing interval between pulses of, say, minutes for this particular application.

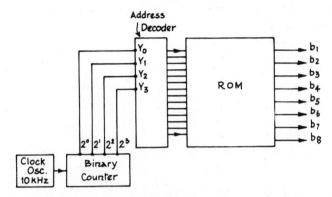

Fig 3.21 Use of ROM to act a modulo-N counter or pulse waveform generator.

Another truth table implementation by a ROM is illustrated in Fig. 3.21. Here the ROM is effectively being used to produce a variable division of the pulse output of the clock oscillator. During programming the bit 1 line may be programmed so that it changes logic state at each new address, bit 2 line so that it changes logic state after 2 addresses, bit 3 line so that it changes logic state after 4 addresses. The waveforms produced on these bit lines are shown in Fig. 3.21(a), (b) and (c) during the 'read' operation. Of course, the idea may be extended to produce other divisions on, say, bit lines 4, 5 and 6, but note that division by even numbers only is possible using this technique since the ROM address remains constant during the periodic time of the clock pulse. Note that the waveform sequence will repeat itself when the binary counter resets (in this case on the 16th clock pulse).

By suitable programming of, say, the bit 7 and 8 lines, pulse waveforms of variable or constant mark-to-space ratio may be generated by the ROM, see waveforms (d) and (e) of Fig. 3.21. Thus the ROM may be used to provide a unique waveform source that may, for example, be used as a test waveform for a digital communication or control system.

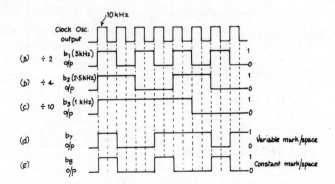

Fig. 3.22 Possible waveform outputs for arrangement of Fig. 3.21.

Character Generator

Alphanumeric characters that are displayed on the screen of a visual display unit are constructed from a series of dots having a size equal to the area of the scanning electron beam of the display c.r.t. The characters are arranged to fit into a standard size dot matrix which is commonly 5×9, see Fig. 3.23. The logic signals that produce the dots making up the displayed

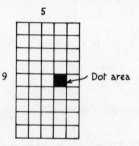

Fig. 3.23 5 × 9 dot matrix.

character may be permanently stored in a ROM or so called 'character generator' and a basic arrangement is illustrated in Fig. 3.24.

This arrangement stores sufficient binary logic levels to produce 96

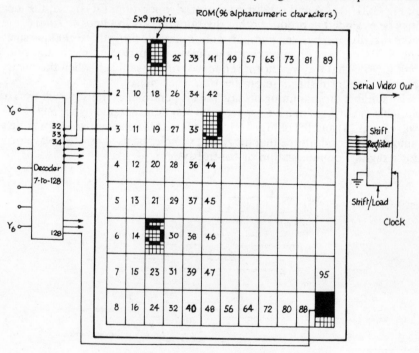

Fig. 3.24 Basic character generator (ROM)

alphanumeric characters and a few examples are shown on the diagram. As each dot matrix stores 45 bits (5 × 9) of information, a total of 96 × 45 = 4320 bits of information will be stored within the ROM.

The particular characters to be written on the screen are selected by the 7-bit code applied to the decoder, the output of which acts as the address for each dot matrix. A 7 to 128 line decoder will specify 128 addresses but only 96 of these are used. In order to construct any character on the screen, the binary logic levels stored in the **9 matrix rows** must be fed to the c.r.t. in **serial form** on **9 consecutive line scans** (see Chapter 6 for further details). Since the 9 matrix rows of any stored character all correspond to the same 7-bit code applied to the address decoder, it follows that additional addresses must be supplied to the ROM to identify each matrix row.

The diagram of Fig. 3.25 shows the matrix row addressing of a diode matrix ROM for a **single** character (the upper case letter A). There are 9 address lines (one for each matrix row) and 5-bit lines (5 × 9). Each matrix row is addressed in sequence by placing a LOW on the address line commencing with x_1 and finishing with x_9, thereby producing a sequence of 9 5-bit parallel data words at the ROM output. Table 3.3 shows the sequential matrix row addressing and the corresponding output data words, where logic $0 = 0V$ and logic $1 = +5V$. By noting the geometry of the pattern of 1s one should be able to make out the letter A.

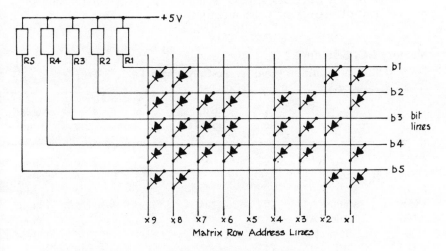

Fig. 3.25 5 × 9 diode matrix ROM producing the letter A.

As previously mentioned, in order to produce the characters on the screen the output bits of each word must be supplied to the c.r.t. in serial form. This is achieved by the use of a PSIO shift register, see Fig. 3.24 and also discussed in Chapter 6.

Line Scan No.	Address Line LOW	Output Bits				
		b_1	b_2	b_3	b_4	b_5
1	x_1	0	0	1	0	0
2	x_2	0	1	0	1	0
3	x_3	1	0	0	0	1
4	x_4	1	0	0	0	1
5	x_5	1	1	1	1	1
6	x_6	1	0	0	0	1
7	x_7	1	0	0	0	1
8	x_8	0	0	0	0	0
9	x_9	0	0	0	0	0 Word 9

Table 3.3 Output words of character generator matrix producing the letter A

Programme Storage

Another important application for ROMs is with programme storage. Control programmes associated with such items as automatic washing machines, pocket calculators, data terminals, video recorders, industrial process control *etc* may be permanently stored in a ROM.

Memory I.C. Selection

Some details of common memory i.cs. are given Table 3.4

I.C.	Type	Family	Bit Capacity	Con-figuration	No. of Pins	Access Time
82S16	Static RAM	TTL	256	256×1	16	50 ns
HEF4720B	Static RAM	CMOS	256	256×1	16	560 ns
10422	Static RAM	ECL	1024	256×4	24	22 ns
8X350	Static RAM	TTL	2048	256×8	22	40 ns
10470	Static RAM	ECL	4096	4096×1	18	35 ns
4256–15	Dynamic RAM		262144	262144×1	16	150 ns
82S23	PROM	TTL	256	32×8	16	50 ns
10149	PROM	ECL	1024	256×4	16	20 ns
82S183	PROM	TTL	8192	1024×8	24	60 ns
2708	EPROM	NMOS	8192	1024×8	24	450 ns
2532	EPROM	NMOS	32768	4096×8	24	450 ns
3400	EAROM		4096	1024×4	22	900 ns

Table 3.4 Memory selection

CHAPTER 4

ANALOGUE AND DIGITAL CONVERSION

Analogue and Digital Information

UNTIL MORE RECENT years most forms of information transferring equipment utilised **analogue** techniques. In analogue systems the information to be processed or conveyed is represented by signal voltages or currents which are simulated replicas of the source information. Common examples include the public telephone network and radio/television broadcasting.

Nowadays, digital methods of transferring or processing information is rapidly gaining favour over analogue techniques in all branches of electronics and communications. When digital techniques are employed, information is conveyed by pulses of voltage or current which have discrete levels only; most systems using just **2 levels**, one of which is zero. Most forms of information that need to be conveyed are of analogue nature whether it be speech or light patterns, the pressure in a remote gas main, the temperature in a furnace or the position of a cutting tool *etc*. Thus in order to digitise such information, **analogue-to-digital conversion** is required. After this has been carried out in a communication system, the digital pulses of voltage or current may be sent directly along cables, modulate a carrier for transmission over wire or through space, modulate a light source for conveyance by optical fibres or be converted into voice frequency signals for transmission over analogue links. Upon receipt of the digitised information, it may be required to convert the information back into its original analogue form, *e.g.* when the information is to be displayed by an analogue instrument or processed by an analogue system. Thus **digital-to-analogue conversion** will be necessary.

Two examples of digital techniques are considered in Fig. 4.1 relating to the measurement of temperature with the aid of a thermocouple. In Fig. 4.1(a) the analogue voltage output of the thermocouple which is proportional to temperature is only of the order of milli-volts and is thus amplified before being applied via a 'sample and hold' circuit ot the A–D stage which converts the signal into a series of digital pulses. These pulses are

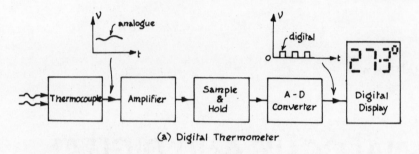

(a) Digital Thermometer

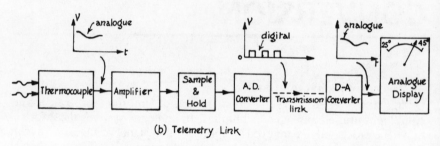

(b) Telemetry Link

Fig. 4.1 Measuring temperature using digital techniques.

then fed to a numeric-type display or alternatively may be fed to a computer for analysis and the temperature reading outputted by a printer.

The arrangement of Fig. 4.1(b) is similar up to the A–D converter but its pulse output is now transmitted over a communication channel which is the basis of measurement at a distance (telemetry). When the pulses are received at the end of the link, they may be converted back into analogue form by the use of a D–A converter to produce the display on the analogue instrument. In both cases, the 'sample and hold' stage is required to sample the analogue signal at appropriate instants and to hold its value whilst A–D conversion takes place.

Reasons for using Digital Techniques

The main advantages of employing digital techniques are as follows:

1) The 2-state devices used in the processing of the 2-level digital type signals do not have to detect precise voltage levels thus non-linearity in the signal path has less effect than in an analogue system. As a result the operation performance and accuracy is more consistent. Also, 2-state devices are more reliable as less power is dissipated in the device.

2) The effects of noise and interference is much reduced in a digital system since it is only necessary to detect the presence of the 2 logic levels. Whenever the noise reaches a level that is likely to cause errors,

the digital pulses can be **regenerated.** This is not possible in analogue systems where the effect of noise or interference is to permanently degrade the signal.

3) The transmission of digital information can be much quicker than equivalent analogue information. For example, in the transmission of speech the time required for someone to say 'too' is about 0·5 secs whereas the coded digital equivalent may be conveyed in less than a microsecond. Also, different digitised information can be allocated separate time slots thus interleaving in time the different information signals. The main disadvantage of digital transmission methods is that they require a greater bandwidth than an equivalent analogue transmission.

SIGNAL SAMPLING AND QUANTISING

Conversion of analogue signals into digital ones may be broken down into three main steps:

Sampling
Quantising
Coding

These processes will be considered in relation to Fig. 4.2, a brief description of which follows.

Data acquisition systems are used to process analogue signals and convert them into digital form for subsequent processing or analysis by a computer, or for data transmission. The principle is used in industrial process control and engineering or scientific telemetry systems for data logging.

The physical quantity to be measured, *e.g.* pressure, temperature, flow rate, vibration *etc* is fed to a transducer which produces an analogue

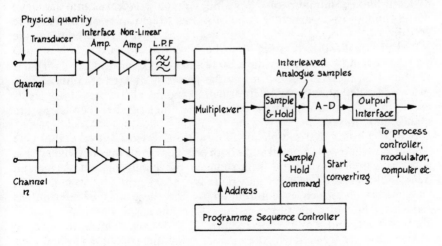

Fig. 4.2 Typical general system for data acquisition.

electrical signal at its output. This signal may be of low voltage or small current and it may have a high source impedance with a single-ended or differential output. The **interface amplifier** is required to convert this to a high level signal voltage (1–10V) which will be suitable for acceptance by later processing stages.

The **non-linear** amplifier is a special circuit which performs mathematical operations on the high level signal, *e.g.* linearisation for transducer non-linearity, squaring, r.m.s. converion *etc* and an operational amplifier may be used for this purpose.

The **low pass filter** is to limit the frequency components in the signal and to reduce noise accompanying the signal. Active filters are used for this task with a cut-off frequency of 20Hz.

The **multiplexer** connects each channel signal in turn to its output to provide time division multiplexing of the transducer signals. The switching address is provided by the programme sequence controller.

In the **sample and hold** stage regular samples of the analogue input are taken which are held steady for a brief period so that A–D conversion can take place without error.

Quantising and **coding** of the analogue samples **takes place in the A–D converter** stage, the output of which is interfaced with the process controller, modulator or computer *etc*.

Timing signals for the sample and hold and A–D converter and addresses for the multiplexer are provided by the **programme sequence controller**. This is a control logic device, often available as a separate i.c. package and sometimes is under the control of a computer.

Sampling and Quantising the Signals

The maximum voltage range of the input to the sample and hold circuit is divided into a number of allowable voltage levels, with each level corresponding to a particular code of pulses to be produced by the A–D converter.

The idea is illustrated in Fig. 4.3 where 8-levels are used. The analogue signal is regularly sampled by the sample and hold circuit and a data signal is produced by the A–D converter to the **nearest standard amplitude**. This process is called **quantising** the information and the allowable voltage levels are known as **quantisation levels** and the intervals between steps the **quantisation intervals**.

It will be noted that sample **a** will produce a code of 111 from the A–D converter, whereas samples **d** and **e** both produce the same code of 010. Thus a certain amount of error is introduced by quantising, known as the **quantisation error**. The error may be reduced by increasing the number of standard levels which is determined by the 'accuracy' or 'resolution' required. The 3-bit code shown requires $2^3 = 8$-levels, a 4-bit code requires $2^4 = 16$-levels and a 5-bit code requires $2^5 = 32$-levels *etc*.

The **sampling frequency** is the number of samples taken per second and the **bit rate** = sampling frequency × number of bits. For example, with a

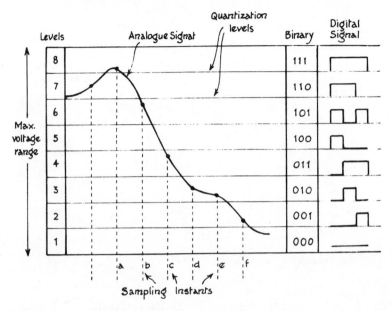

Fig. 4.3 Sampling and quantising a signal.

sampling frequency of 8kHz and an 8-bit code (256 levels) the bit rate =
8000 × 8 = 64 kilo-bits/sec.

Sample & Hold

A basic circuit of a sample and hold i.c. is given in Fig. 4.4 with waveforms
illustrating its action in Fig. 4.5. When the mosfet switch is closed the unit is
in the 'sample' or 'tracking' mode and will follow the changing input signal.
When the switch is open the unit is in the 'hold' mode and retains a sample in

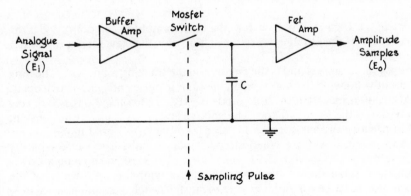

Fig. 4.4 Sample and hold circuit.

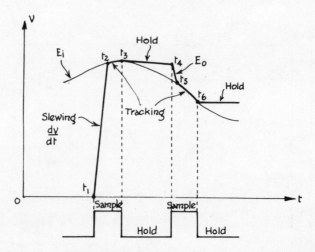

Fig. 4.5 Waveforms illustrating operation of sample and hold circuit.

the form of a voltage held by the storage capacitor C. During the hold mode A–D conversion can take place without error due to input fluctuation. The period of time that C holds its charge depends upon the leakage of the mosfet switch, the input impedance of the following amplifier (low i/p current type) and the internal leakage of the capacitor.

Assume that initially C is uncharged and the switch is open. At instant t_1 the switch is closed by the sample pulse causing C to charge towards the output voltage of the buffer amplifier, finally acquiring the level of the input at instant t_2. The time interval $t_1 - t_2$ is the 'acquisition time' and during this interval the buffer amplifer is 'slewing'. The maximum rate of change of voltage across C is given by:

$$\frac{dv}{dt} = \frac{I_{max}}{C}$$

where I_{max} is the maximum current the buffer amplifier can deliver, C is the capacitance of the storage capacitor and dv/dt is the slew rate of the buffer amplifier.

Between instants t_2 and t_3 the circuit is in the tracking mode, *i.e.* following the input voltage. At instant t_3 when the sample pulse ends, the switch opens and the unit is placed in the hold mode ($t_3 - t_4$). The voltage across C during this period is the sample taken. The voltage level should ideally be constant but in practice droops slightly due to charge leakage ('hold mode voltage droop') but in a well designed circuit is very small (droop rate typically 5mV/second). In Fig. 4.5, the input voltage (E_i) is assumed to be a slowly changing voltage such as that produced by a temperature sensor. At the instant the 'hold' command is given the mosfet switch does not immediately open. Thus there is a small delay before the circut enters the 'hold' mode and

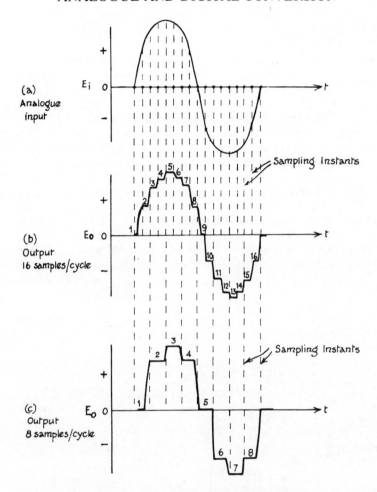

Fig. 4.6 Effect of varying the sample rate on output of sample and hold.

this is due to the time taken for the mosfet device to switch-off. This is called
the **aperture time** and may cause errors.

The diagrams of Fig. 4.6 show the effect on the output of the sample and
hold circuit when the sampling rate is altered, assuming a sine wave input. It
will be seen that the sampling produces 16-levels or samples in Fig. 4.6(b)
but only 8 in Fig. 4.6(c). An important and fundamental question to be asked
about sampling is 'how often must a given signal be sampled in order not to
lose information?' It seems reasonably obvious that all useful information
may be extracted from a slowly changing signal by sampling at a rate which is
faster than any change that occurs, and likewise that if the signal changes
value significantly between samples, information is being lost. The answer is
contained in the well known 'Sampling Theorem'.

Sampling Theorem

The theorem may be stated as follows:

If a continuous bandwidth limited signal contains no frequency components higher than f_c, then the original signal can be completely recovered without distortion if it is sampled at a rate of at least $2f_c$ samples per second.

For a **sine wave** signal this means that it may be completely recovered if at least 2 samples are taken per cycle, thus the original sine wave of Fig. 4.6(a) may be completely recovered with the sampling rates used in Fig. 4.6(b) or (c). When the waveform to be sampled is **complex** then the sampling rate must be **at least 2 times the highest frequency component contained in the wave**.

When only 2 samples per cycle are taken of a sine wave signal it does not immediately appear reasonable that a complete sine wave could be recovered, but this is explained with the aid of Fig. 4.7. Here just 2 samples per cycle are taken and assume that these are coded 111 and 000 by the A–D converter. If these codes are applied to a D–A converter then its voltage output would be as shown, with the levels **a** and **b** corresponding to the coded inputs of 111 and 000. If now the square wave output of the D–A converter,

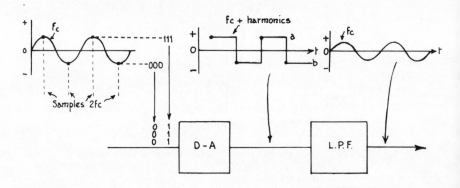

Fig. 4.7 Diagram illustrating 'sampling rule'.

containing f_c, plus harmonics, is fed to a l.p.f. which removes all frequency components above f_c, then a sine wave signal at f_c would remain at the output. In practice, the recovered signal would not be an exact replica because filters do not have an infinitely sharp cut-off and may introduce phase shift in the pass band. The similarity of a signal with its recovered version is enhanced by using a sampling rate somewhat in excess of that given by the sampling theorem.

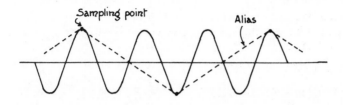

Fig. 4.8 Aliasing.

Fig. 4.8 shows the effect when a sine wave signal is sampled at a rate less than twice per cycle. If the sampled amplitudes are joined together (shown dotted), then after recovery the resultant signal will have a periodic time which is quite different from the original and is an 'alias'. Thus **aliasing** is the result of using too low a sampling rate and introduces distortion into the converted signal.

A–D & D–A CODES

A–D and D–A converters relate analogue and digital values by means of various codes.

Unipolar & Bipolar Converters

Converters that deal with voltages of one polarity only are called **Unipolar**, *e.g.* 0V to +10V or 0V to −10V whereas converters that deal with positive and negative voltages *e.g.* 0V to ±5V are called Bipolar.

Full-Scale Voltage (V_{FS})

The nominal design maximum voltage range of a converter is called the **full-scale voltage**. The maximum output voltage of a converter is always less than V_{FS} by an amount depending upon the code used and the number of bits.

Resolution

The **resolution** of a converter is the smallest analogue change that can be detected or produced by a converter. It is determined by the number of bits (n) and is numerically equal to the value of the l.s.b. For example, an 8-bit converter with a full-scale voltage of 10V will have a resolution of

$$\frac{V_{FS}}{2^n} = \frac{10}{2^8} = 0{\cdot}039V$$

Straight Binary Code

This is the simplest of converter codes and is used in unipolar converters. When a coded bit is at logic 1 it is given a 'weighting' as follows:

1st m.s.b .... $\dfrac{V_{FS}}{2^1}$

2nd m.s.b .... $\dfrac{V_{FS}}{2^2}$

3rd m.s.b .... $\dfrac{V_{FS}}{2^3}$

l.s.b. or n^{th} bit .... $\dfrac{V_{FS}}{2^n}$

The equivalent analogue voltage for the code is the **sum** of the weightings, *i.e.*

$$\frac{V_{FS}}{2} + \frac{V_{FS}}{2^2} + \frac{V_{FS}}{2^3} + \frac{V_{FS}}{2^n} = V_{FS} \left(\frac{1}{2} + \frac{1}{4} + \frac{1}{8} + \frac{1}{2^n} \right)$$

For example, consider a 3-bit converter with a V_{FS} of +10V. The relation between the digital and analogue values would be:

m.s.b.

```
0  0  0 ............................................. = 0V
0  0  1 ................. 10 (⅛)              = +1·25V (Resolution)
0  1  0 ................. 10 (¼)              = +2·5V
0  1  1 ................. 10 (¼ + ⅛)          = +3·75V
1  0  0    ............. 10 (½)              = +5·0V (½ Full-scale)
1  0  1 ................. 10 (½ + ⅛)          = +6·25V
1  1  0 ................. 10 (½ + ¼)          = +7·5V
1  1  1 ................. 10 (½ + ¼ + ⅛)      = + 8·75V (V_max)
```

Binary Off-Set Code

This code is used in some bipolar converters. It is similar to straight binary but with the equivalent output voltage shifted to make binary half full-scale equivalent to analogue zero. When a coded bit is at logic 1 it is given a weighting as follows:

1st m.s.b .... $\dfrac{V_{FS}}{2^0}$

2nd m.s.b .... $\dfrac{V_{FS}}{2^1}$

3rd m.s.b .... $\dfrac{V_{FS}}{2^2}$

l.s.b. or n^{th} bit .... $\dfrac{V_{FS}}{2^{n-1}}$

The relation between digital and analogue values is given by:

$$V_{analgue} = V_{FS} (1 + \tfrac{1}{2} + \tfrac{1}{4} + \tfrac{1}{8} + \tfrac{1}{2^{n-1}} - 1)$$

Consider a 3-bit converter with a V_{FS} of $\pm 5V$:

m.s.b.   l.s.b

0 0 0	....	$5[(0) - 1]$	$= -5V$	$(V_{max}$ negative)
0 0 1	....	$5[(\tfrac{1}{4}) - 1]$	$= -3\cdot 75V$	
0 1 0	....	$5[(\tfrac{1}{2}) - 1]$	$= -2\cdot 5V$	
0 1 1	....	$5[(\tfrac{1}{2} + \tfrac{1}{4}) - 1]$	$= -1\cdot 25V$	
1 0 0	....	$5[(1) - 1]$	$= 0V$	($\tfrac{1}{2}$ Full-scale)
1 0 1	....	$5[(1 + \tfrac{1}{4}) - 1]$	$= +1\cdot 25V$	
1 1 0	....	$5[(1 + \tfrac{1}{2}) - 1]$	$= +2\cdot 5V$	
1 1 1	....	$5[(1 + \tfrac{1}{2} + \tfrac{1}{4}) - 1]$	$= +3\cdot 75V$	$(V_{max}$ positive)

$$\text{Resolution} = \frac{10}{2^3} = 1\cdot 25V$$

Binary Twos Complement

This alternative bipolar code is similar to binary off-set but with the m.s.b. complemented. When a coded bit is at logic 1 it is given a weighting as follows:

$$\text{1st m.s.b} \dots\dots\dots\dots\dots\dots\dots\dots\dots \frac{V_{FS}}{2^0}$$

$$\text{2nd m.s.b} \dots\dots\dots\dots\dots\dots\dots\dots\dots \frac{V_{FS}}{2^1}$$

$$\text{3rd m.s.b} \dots\dots\dots\dots\dots\dots\dots\dots\dots \frac{V_{FS}}{2^2}$$

$$\text{l.s.b. or } n^{th} \text{ bit} \dots\dots\dots\dots\dots\dots\dots \frac{V_{FS}}{2^{n-1}}$$

The relation between analogue and digital values is given by:

$$V_{analgue} = V_{FS} \left(\tfrac{1}{2} + \tfrac{1}{4} + \tfrac{1}{8} + \tfrac{1}{2^{n-1}} - 1 \right)$$

(2nd m.s.b.   3rd m.s.b. n^{th} m.s.b.   m.s.b)

Consider a 3-bit code with a V_{FS} of $\pm 5V$:

m.s.b.   l.s.b

0 0 0	....		$= 0V$	
0 0 1	....	$5 (\tfrac{1}{4})$	$= +1\cdot 25V$	
0 1 0	....	$5 (\tfrac{1}{2})$	$= +2\cdot 5V$	
0 1 1	....	$5 (\tfrac{1}{2} + \tfrac{1}{4})$	$= +3\cdot 75V$	$(V_{max}$ positive)
1 0 0	....	$5 (-1)$	$= -5\cdot 0V$	$(V_{max}$ negative)
1 0 1	....	$5 (\tfrac{1}{4} - 1)$	$= -3\cdot 75V$	
1 1 0	....	$5 (\tfrac{1}{2} - 1)$	$= -2\cdot 5V$	
1 1 1	....	$5 (\tfrac{1}{2} + \tfrac{1}{4} - 1)$	$= -1\cdot 25V$	

Resolution $= \dfrac{10}{2} = 1{\cdot}25\text{V}$

D–A CONVERTERS

D–A converters will be considered first as some A–D converters use a D–A converter in their feedback loop.

Binary Weighted D–A Converter

A circuit diagram of a 4-bit binary weighted D–A converter is given in Fig. 4.9. This arrangement uses an OP-AMP as a summing amplifier with binary weighted input resistor values, *i.e.* values which increase sequentially by multiples of 2, R – 2R – 4R – 8R – 16R *etc.* S1 – S4 are electronic switches that are operated by the digital input. When a logic 1 is applied to any digital input line, the switch associated with that line is connected to the reference voltage source; if a logic 0 is applied the switch is connected to the earth line.

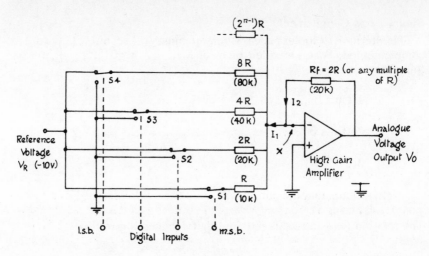

Fig. 4.9 4-bit binary weighted D–A converter.

Point X is a virtual earth. With all switches closed (as shown) corresponding to a digital input of 1111, the current I_1 is given by:

$$I_1 = \frac{V_R}{R} + \frac{V_R}{2R} + \frac{V_R}{4R} + \frac{V_R}{8R}$$

and the current I_2 is given by:

$$I_2 = \frac{V_0}{R_f}$$

Since X is the virtual earth $I_2 = -I_1$ (Kirchoff's) therefore:

$$\frac{V_0}{R_f} = -\left(\frac{V_R}{R} + \frac{V_R}{2R} + \frac{V_R}{4R} + \frac{V_R}{8R}\right)$$

or $V_0 = -R_f\left(\frac{V_R}{R} + \frac{V_R}{2R} + \frac{V_R}{4R} + \frac{V_R}{8R}\right)$.

Thus the amplifier 'sums' the sources with a binary weighting provided by the resistors.

Consider now the output voltage from the OP-AMP for the following examples of digital input, assuming that $R = 2R$, $V_R = -10V$ and that the OP-AMP will operate with supply line voltages up to, say, 50V.

Digital Input 1111

$$V_0 = -2R\left(\frac{-10}{R} + \frac{-10}{2R} + \frac{-10}{4R} + \frac{-10}{8R}\right)$$

$V_0 = +37{\cdot}5V$ (V_{max})

Digital Input 0001

$$V_0 = -2R\left(\frac{-10}{8R}\right)$$

$V_0 = +2{\cdot}5V$ (Resolution)

Digital Input 1000

$$V_0 = -2R\left(\frac{-10}{R}\right)$$

$V_0 = +20V$ (half full-scale)

It will be noted that the output voltage in this unipolar circuit is of positive polarity. By using a reference voltage of positive polarity, *e.g.* $+10V$, output voltages of negative polarity may be obtained. Note that the summed input is applied to the inverting terminal of the OP-AMP. The negative sign in the expression used above allows for this fact.

The switches can be bipolar or fet. The main disadvantage with this circuit is the wide range of resistor values required for a high resolution converter which makes temperature matching difficult. For example, with a 10-bit converter if the smallest value is 1k-ohm, the largest resistor value will be 512k-ohm. To achieve good linearity and accuracy, close tolerance resistors would have to be used which 'tracked' with temperature. Binary weighted D–A converters are often used in non-critical applications, *e.g.* in the remote control of volume, brightness *etc* in a television receiver.

R-2R Ladder D–A Converter

The R-2R D–A converter, see Fig. 4.10, uses 2 resistors per bit but only

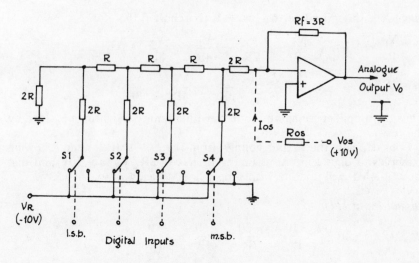

Fig. 4.10 4-bit R–2R D–A converter.

values of R and 2R are required. The contribution of each bit when set at logic 1 is as follows:

$$
\begin{array}{ll}
\text{1st m.s.b.} \dots\dots\dots\dots\dots\dots\dots\dots\dots\dots\dots\dots & \dfrac{V_R}{3} \\[2mm]
\text{2nd m.s.b.} \dots\dots\dots\dots\dots\dots\dots\dots\dots\dots\dots\dots & \dfrac{V_R}{6} \\[2mm]
\text{3rd m.s.b.} \dots\dots\dots\dots\dots\dots\dots\dots\dots\dots\dots\dots & \dfrac{V_R}{12} \\[2mm]
\text{4th m.s.b.} \dots\dots\dots\dots\dots\dots\dots\dots\dots\dots\dots\dots & \dfrac{V_R}{24} \\[2mm]
\text{l.s.b. or } n^{\text{th}} \text{ bit} \dots\dots\dots\dots\dots\dots\dots\dots\dots\dots & \dfrac{V_R}{3 \times 2^{n-1}}
\end{array}
$$

In general the output voltage V_0 is given by:

$$V_0 = -\frac{R_f}{2R} \left(\frac{V_R}{3} + \frac{V_R}{6} + \frac{V_R}{12} + \frac{V_R}{24} \cdots \cdots \cdots \frac{V_R}{3 \times 2^{n-1}} \right)$$

Consider the output voltage from the OP-AMP for the following digital inputs, assuming that $V_R = -10V$ and $R_f = 3R$.

Digital Input 1111

$$V_0 = -\frac{3R}{2R} \left(\frac{-10}{3} + \frac{-10}{6} + \frac{-10}{12} + \frac{-10}{24} \right)$$

$$= +9 \cdot 375V \; (V_{max})$$

Digital Input 1000

$$V_0 = - \frac{3R}{2R} \left(\frac{-10}{3} \right)$$

$$= +5V \text{ (half full scale)}$$

Digital Input 0001

$$V_0 = - \frac{3R}{2R} \left(\frac{-10}{24} \right)$$

$$= +0 \cdot 625V \text{ (resolution)}$$

Digital Input 0111

$$V_0 = - \frac{3R}{2R} \left(\frac{-10}{6} + \frac{-10}{12} + \frac{-10}{24} \right)$$

$$= +4 \cdot 375V$$

The above illustrates unipolar operation of the converter. Note that if output voltages of opposite polarity are required, the polarity of the reference voltage should be reversed.

Bipolar Operation

To produce output voltages of either polarity using 'binary off-set' coding, a constant off-set current I_{OS} is supplied as shown dotted. The resistor R_{OS} is selected to provide an I_{OS} equal to the current of the m.s.b. Whether or not the m.s.b. is present in an input code determines the polarity of the output voltage, therefore the m.s.b. is called the 'sign' bit. In general the output voltage V_0 is given by:

$$V_0 = - \frac{R_f}{2R} \left(\frac{V_R}{3} + \frac{V_R}{6} + \frac{V_R}{12} + \frac{V_R}{24} \cdots \cdots + \frac{V_{OS}}{3} \right)$$

N.B. include the polarities of V_R and V_{OS} in the expression, examples:

Digital Input 1010

$$V_0 = - \frac{3R}{2R} \left(\frac{-10}{3} + \frac{-10}{12} + \frac{10}{3} \right)$$

$$= +1 \cdot 25V$$

Digital Input 0100

$$V_0 = - \frac{3R}{2R} \left(\frac{-10}{6} + \frac{10}{3} \right)$$

$$= -2 \cdot 5V$$

The R-2R ladder D–A converter is the most common and can easily be extended to as many bits as are required. The absolute values of the resistors is not so important as the ratio, which needs to be exact. Electronic switches are employed and precision reference voltage sources are normally included on the i.c. device.

A–D CONVERTERS

A large number of methods for converting analogue signals to digital data exist and two basic techniques are described in this section.

Counter Ramp A–D Converter

The basic schematic of this method is illustrated in Fig. 4.11. Conversion commences with a 'start signal' which resets the binary counter to zero. At this instant the output from the D–A converter is zero and $V_1 > V_2$. The comparator gives out a logic 1 which enables the AND gate and allows clock pulses to be fed to the binary counter. As the clock pulses are counted, the output from the D–A converter rises in 'staircase' fashion. When V_2 is just slightly greater than V_1, the comparator gives out a logic 0 which disables the AND gate and thus inhibits the clock input to the counter. Conversion is now complete and the **digital output is the binary number stored in counter** at this instant.

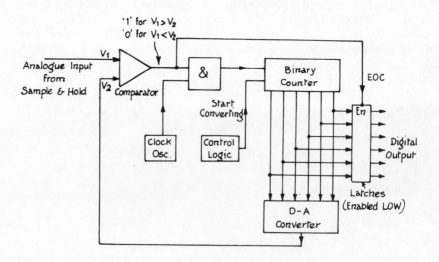

Fig. 4.11 Counter ramp A–D converter.

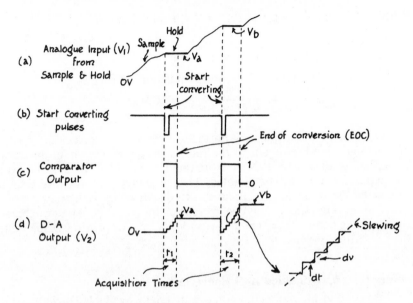

Fig. 4.12 Waveforms explaining action of counter ramp A–D converter.

Waveforms illustrating the operation are given in Fig. 4.12 where two levels of input are considered, V_a and V_b. The diagram serves to illustrate the need for synchronisation of the Sample and Hold circuit and the A–D converter, *i.e.* the sample and hold circuit should enter the 'hold mode' at the instant that the 'start converting signal' is given. Also conversion must be completed by the end of the hold mode interval.

Acquisition Time

The **acquisition time** of the converter will depend upon the **magnitude of the sampled analogue input** and the **clock frequency**, see intervals t_1 and t_2 of Fig. 4.12. Since the D–A converter changes by the weight of the l.s.b. for each clock pulse, the **slew rate** of the converter will be:

$$\frac{L.S.B.}{\frac{1}{f_c}},$$

where f_c = clock frequency and L.S.B. is expressed in volts.

Example:

The l.s.b. of a 10-bit converter with a V_{FS} of 10V

$$= \frac{10}{2^{10}} = 9 \cdot 77 \text{mV}.$$

With a clock frequency of 1MHz, the slew rate $\rightleftharpoons 9 \cdot 77 \text{mV}/\mu\text{s}$.

With an analogue input of, say, 1V the acquisition time

$$= \frac{1}{9 \cdot 77 \times 10^{-3}} = 102 \cdot 4 \mu s.$$

With an analogue input of 10V, the acquisition time

$$= \frac{10}{9 \cdot 77 \times 10^{-3}} = 1024 \mu s.$$

The acquisition time quoted is normally given for the worst case, *i.e.* when the analogue input is equal to the full-scale voltage (V_{FS}). In the above example it is, of course, $1024\mu s$. Note that if the clock frequency is halved, the acquisition time will be doubled. The advantages of this converter is its simplicity, low cost and good accuracy. Its disadvantage is the slow speed of conversion. The speed may be increased by using an **up-down binary counter**. The counter then counts up or down from its previous value rather than resetting to zero.

Successive Approximation A–D Converter

This is one of the more common commercially available converters with a superior speed performance to the counter ramp type. The diagram of Fig. 4.13 shows the basic arrangement. Conversion commences with a 'start converting' pulse into the control logic and ends 'n' clock pulses later when the digital output is valid. Consider a 4-bit converter.

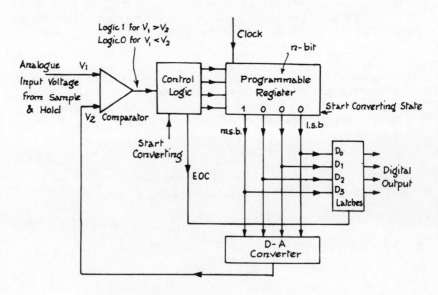

Fig. 4.13 Successive approximation A–D converter.

The 'start converting' pulse causes the control logic to set the register to half full-scale (1000) so that the output of the D–A converter $V_2 = V_{FS}/2$. If $V_1 > V_2$, the logic 1 from the comparator causes the control logic to set the register on the next clock pulse to 1100, *i.e.* the register output is increased by half again so that $V_2 = 3/4V_{FS}$. If $V_1 < V_2$, the logic 0 from the comparator causes the control logic to set the register on the next clock pulse to give an output of 1010, *i.e.* the count is reduced to half way between $V_{FS}/2$ and $3/4$ V_{FS}; thus $V_2 = 5/8$ V_{FS}. This process continues until the l.s.b. is used (logic 1) or left alone (logic 0).

When the l.s.b. has been tested, the control logic sends out an 'end of conversion' signal (EOC) which causes the output latches (D-type flip-flops) to operate, placing the valid binary data word at the converter output. It will be seen that the converter successively approximates the analogue input into an equivalent digital word, tests it by comparison, tries again and at each attempt gets closer to the true digitised value.

The waveforms of Fig. 4.14 illustrate the operation for a 4-bit converter having a full-scale of 10V when a sampled level of 6·8V (V_1) is applied to the input. At the end of the conversion period the data word 1011 will be latched into the converter output. This, of course, is the quantised form of the analogue input of 6·8V and is accurate to $\pm\frac{1}{2}$ l.s.b. (0·625V). Another example is given in Fig. 4.14 using an analogue input of 3·1V. Here, at the end of the conversion period, the data word 0101 will be latched into the converter output.

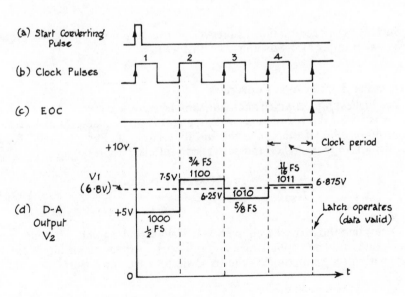

Fig. 4.14 Waveforms illustrating operation of successive approximation A–D converter (4-bit) (input sampled level = 6·8V).

Acquisition Time

With a successive approximation A–D converter, the acquisition time is independent of the magnitude of the analogue input. **The time is the same for all levels of input** and is given by:

Acquisition Time $\simeq$ Number of Bits × Clock Periodic Time.

For the 4-bit converter considered in Fig. 4.14 and 4.15, the acquisition time = 4 × clock pulse period. With a clock frequency of 0·5MHz, the acquisition would be 8μs. In practice it would be slightly in excess of this figure due to propagation delays in the comparator, control logic, register, D–A converter and latch.

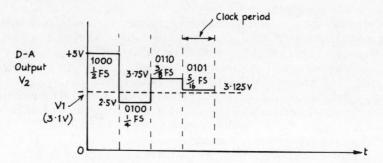

Fig. 4.15 Successive approximation converter with sampled analogue input level of 3·1V.

Successive approximation 12-bit A–D converters are available with total conversion times of 4–8μs and ultra fast at 1μs.

Conversion Rate of A–D Converters

The highest rate at which analogue samples may be converted into digital codes is called the **conversion** or **throughput rate.** It is determined by the acquisition time of the converter and its reciprocal. For example, if the acquisition time = 200μs, the conversion rate is:

$$\frac{1}{200 \times 10^{-6}} = 5000 \text{ conversions/sec.}$$

Problem

Determine the highest frequency sine wave signal, sampled 16 times per cycle, that could be applied to an A–D converter with an acquisition time of 2μs, without it going outside the bandwidth of the converter.

Solution

Conversion rate of converter $= \dfrac{1}{2 \times 10^{-6}} = 500000$ conversions/sec.

Highest frequency sine wave signal $= \dfrac{500000}{16} = 31250\text{Hz}.$

i.e. 31250Hz represents the bandwidth limit of the converter **for the sampling rate used.** If the number of samples taken per cycle is reduced, the bandwidth limit will be extended.

OTHER CONVERTER TERMS

Dynamic Range

The dynamic range of a converter may be expressed as a ratio of:

$$\frac{\text{Maximum Voltage}}{\text{Resolution Voltage}}$$

For example, the resolution voltage of a 4-bit A–D converter with a V_{FS} of 10V $= 10/2^4 = 0{\cdot}625\text{V}$, corresponding to an output code of 0001. The maximum input voltage is 10V which would be quantised to 1111. Thus the dynamic range $= 10/0{\cdot}625 = 16 : 1$ or in dBs, $20\text{Log}16 = 24\text{dB}$. Since a factor of 2 corresponds to approximately 6dB, the dynamic range in dBs is given by number of bits $\times$ 6dB.

Linearity

An ideal transfer charactersitic of a converter is shown in Fig. 4.16(a) **Linearity error** is the maximum deviation from a striaght line drawn between the end points of the converter transfer function, see Fig. 4.16(b). The error may be expressed as a percentage of Full-Scale or as a fraction of the l.s.b. size. The error in a good converter is $\pm\frac{1}{2}$ l.s.b.

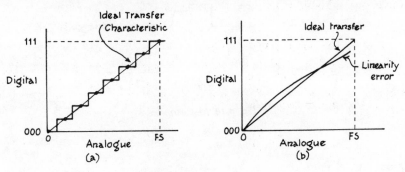

Fig. 4.16 Converter linearity.

Offset and Scale Factor Errors

These errors are shown in Fig. 4.17. **Offset error** is the error by which the transfer function fails to pass through the origin, referred to as the analogue axis. This is normally adjustable to zero in available converters. **Scale Factor**

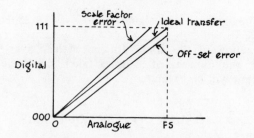

Fig. 4.17 Off-set and scale factor errors.

or **Gain Error** is the difference in slope between the actual transfer function and the ideal expressed as a percentage. This is adjustable to zero in available converters.

Monotonicity

A monotonic converter is one which does not miss a step or show a decrease as the input to the converter is increased from zero to its rated maximum. The diagram of Fig. 4.18 illustrates a non-monotonic output.

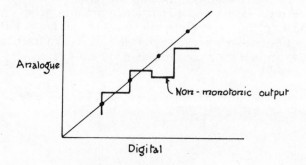

Fig. 4.18 Monotonicity.

Quantising Error

This term has been considered previously but is explained more fully using the diagram of Fig. 4.19. **Quantising error** arises from the need to use a finite number of digital levels for an infinite number of analogue values. The transfer function shown above is ideal with analogue 'decision' levels at 0·5, 1·5, 2·5, 3·5 *etc*. The decision levels are set at values which 'bracket' the 'true' levels of analogue inputs of 1, 2, 3, 4 *etc*. The analogue 1 level corresponds to digital 001 and is half-way between decision levels 0·5 and

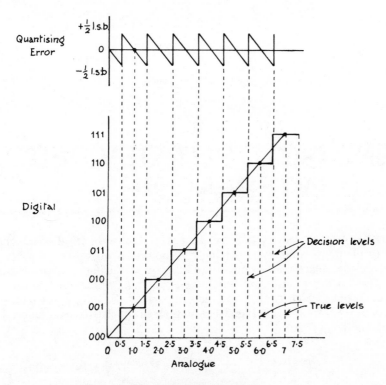

Fig. 4.19 Quantising error.

1·5. Thus analogue values between 0·5 and 1·5 would be quantised to 001. The quantising error would be zero with exactly 1·0 input and would increase for input values above and below this, approaching $-\frac{1}{2}$ l.s.b. or $+\frac{1}{2}$ l.s.b. as the voltage approaches 0·5 or 1·5 respectively. The quantising error thus takes the form of a sawtooth wave.

CHAPTER 5

INPUT-OUTPUT DEVICES AND INTERFACING

A DIGITAL ELECTRONIC system such as that used in automatically controlled factory plant operates by collecting information from various sensors or **input devices** placed at strategic points around the factory, processing/analysing the information and communicating it in suitable form to various **output devices** which control the factory process. Examples of input and output devices are given in Fig. 5.1, a number of which will be considered in this chapter.

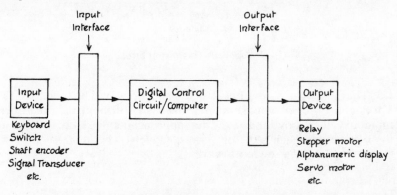

Fig. 5.1 Input/output devices and their interfacing.

Interface circuits, in general, may be called upon to perform a large variety of tasks. For example, if the input device produces an analogue signal, A–D conversion will be required so as to present the signal to the Digital Circuit in a form that it can handle. Similarly, if an analogue output device is employed, D–A conversion will be necessary. Thus A–D and D–A are common examples of interfacing circuits.

Some input devices generate digital type signals, but these may be of too small a voltage, of poor shape or in a code that is not acceptable to the digital circuit or system. Thus amplification, pulse-sharpening or code conversion may be required of the interface circuit. When a large power transducer such as a motor is used as an output device, the interface circuit will normally include some power amplification since digital circuits are essentially low power sources.

In summary it may be said that an interface circuit performs such tasks as code conversion, A–D and D–A conversion, level shifting, impedance matching, amplification, pulse shaping *etc*, and therefore, it 'conditions' input signals to the digital circuit or output signals from it.

INPUT DEVICES AND THEIR INTERFACING

Switch Debouncer

When mechanical switches are used to provide logical signal inputs to digital circuits, 'contact bounce' which occurs as contacts close can lead to problems. The effect of the bounce, due to the elasticity of the metal contacts, is to produce several pulses from the switch when only one should have been produced, see Fig. 5.2 and may last up to several ms.

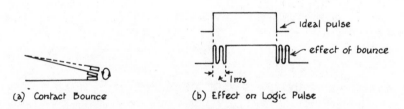

(a) Contact Bounce   (b) Effect on Logic Pulse

Fig. 5.2 Contact bounce.

With two-way switches, contact bounce can occur before coming to rest in the open or closed position. Contact bounce is tolerable when simply applying d.c. levels to test the truth table of a logic gate, but when the d.c. pulse is the input to a counter for example, false counts can be produced. Two methods will be described to eliminate the effects of the bounce.

Use of S-R Flip-Flop

In an S-R flip-flop if the Q output is set at logic 1, the application of a logic 1 to the SET input (RESET at logic 0) will have no effect on the Q output, *i.e.* it will remain at logic 1 (see chapter 2). Thus an S-R flip-flop may be used to eliminate multipulse output and the principle is shown in Fig. 5.3.

On the first 'make' (S1 'on'), the Q output of the flip-flop is set at logic 1 and the remaining bounces have no effect. Similarly, when S1 is set to the 'off' position the Q output is reset at logic 0 and the remaining bounces have not effect. The flip-flop does not, of course, eliminate the switch bounce but only its effect on the output from the interface circuit.

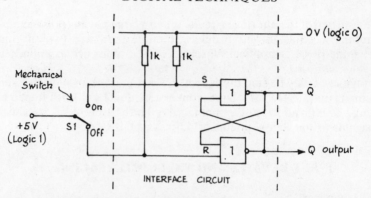

Fig. 5.3 Use of S–R flip-flop to eliminate contact bounce.

Use of CMOS Schmitt Inverter

A switch debouncer for contacts that are normally open using a Schmitt inverter is given in Fig. 5.4 and waveforms explaining the circuit operation is given in Fig. 5.5. The time constant of C1,R1 should be at least three times the worst expected total bounce period. For the values stated the time

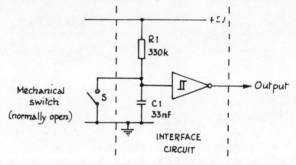

Fig. 5.4 Use of Schmitt inverter to eliminate the effects of contact bounce.

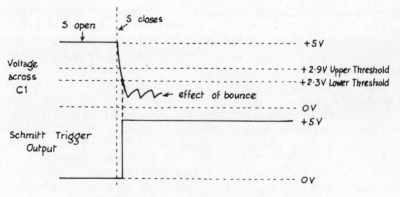

Fig. 5.5 Waveforms explaining operation of Fig. 5.4.

constant of 10·9ms would be adequate for total bounce periods up to 3ms.

When the switch is open, C1 is charged to +5V and the output from the Schmitt trigger is LOW (0V). When the switch closes, C1 commences to discharge rapidly via the switch and the voltage across C1 falls below +2·3V causing the Schmitt trigger output to go HIGH. Contact bounce has no effect on the output due to the chosen time constant, since C1 must recharge to above +2·9V to cause the Schmitt trigger output to go LOW. A circuit for switch contacts that are normally closed is given in Fig. 5.6 which operates in a similar manner to that described.

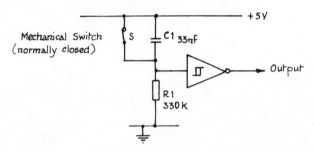

Fig. 5.6 Circuit for switch contacts that are normally closed.

Shaft Encoder

A **shaft encoder** is an input device which produces an **output digital signal** that has a digitised value proportional to the **angular position of a shaft** or to **linear position** when a lead screw and nut are used. It consists of a coded disc which rotates with the shaft, converting angular position into a direct digital read out. There are two types of shaft encoder.

Absolute Encoder

With an absolute encoder, the disc has a number of concentric tracks with a code pattern formed upon it, see Fig. 5.7. The disc may take the form of a photographic plate where the dark areas are used to interrupt a light beam. The number of concentric tracks used will depend upon the resolution required. With 4 tracks, as shown, a 4-bit encoder results and will provide an angular resolution of:

$$\frac{360}{2^4} = 22 \cdot 5°$$

If 8 tracks are used, an 8-bit encoder results giving an angular resolution of:

$$\frac{360}{2^8} = 1 \cdot 4°.$$

Associated with each track will be a light beam source (l.e.d) and a light sensor (photo-transistor).

DIGITAL TECHNIQUES

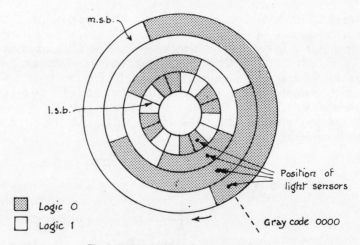

Fig. 5.7 Absolute shaft encoder (4-bit).

The binary code is not suitable for coded discs since when 2 or more bits change state, it is not always possible to ensure that they change together (due to positional tolerances of the light sensors) resulting in possible false read-outs. Commonly a **Gray code** is used where only 1-bit changes at each transition and this is used in the coding of the disc in Fig. 5.7. Comparison between Gray and Binary codes are shown in Table 5.1.

Gray Code				Binary Code				Decimal
0	0	0	0	0	0	0	0	0
0	0	0	1	0	0	0	1	1
0	0	1	1	0	0	1	0	2
0	0	1	0	0	0	1	1	3
0	1	1	0	0	1	0	0	4
0	1	1	1	0	1	0	1	5
0	1	0	1	0	1	1	0	6
0	1	0	0	0	1	1	1	7
1	1	0	0	1	0	0	0	8
1	1	0	1	1	0	0	1	9
1	1	1	1	1	0	1	0	10
1	1	1	0	1	0	1	1	11
1	0	1	0	1	1	0	0	12
1	0	1	1	1	1	0	1	13
1	0	0	1	1	1	1	0	14
1	0	0	0	1	1	1	1	15

Table 5.1 Gray Code

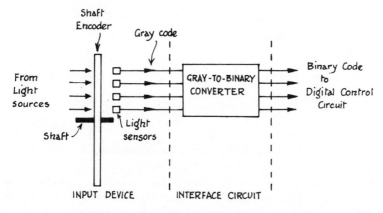

Fig. 5.8 Use of interface circuit with shaft encoder.

Note that the Gray code is cyclic, *i.e.* the last code in the table (1000) is next to the first code (0000) and produces only one digit change as the shaft completes and starts a new revolution. With Gray coding, a logic 1 in any column does not have a fixed weighting (as with binary) thus the code cannot easily be used for arithmetic. Thus in a digital system, the Gray code output of the shaft encoder must be converted into binary code, see Fig. 5.8.

Gray-to Binary Converter (Decoder)
Decoding the Gray code output of the shaft encoder may be achieved using a logic arrangement of EX-OR gates as shown in Fig. 5.9. An alternative decoding arrangement that may be used makes use of a 'look-up'

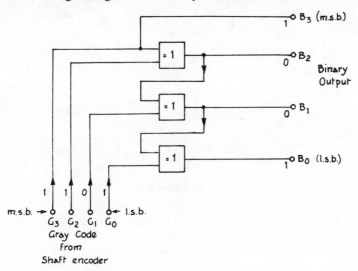

Fig. 5.9 Arrangement for a 4-bit Gray-to-binary decoder.

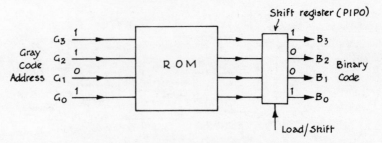

Fig. 5.10 Use of ROM for decoding.

table stored in a ROM. The Gray code may be used to provide the address for the ROM which holds the corresponding binary code for that unique address, see Fig. 5.10. This type of decoding is suitable when shaft encoders of 8-bits or more are used.

Incremental Shaft Encoder

The coded disc for an incremental shaft encoder is shown in Fig. 5.11(a) and requires only one set of equally spaced alternate light and dark areas, or equally spaced radial lines. An extra track with only one mark or radial line

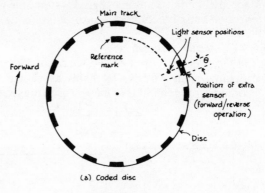

(a) Coded disc

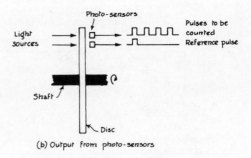

(b) Output from photo-sensors

Fig. 5.11 Incremental shaft encoder.

is used as a reference. As before, light sources and photo-transistors may be used to sense the marks or lines.

When the shaft is rotating, pulses will be obtained from the light sensors as shown in Fig. 5.11(b). The pulses from the main track will be continuous at a rate of 16 per revolution with, say, a dark area corresponding to logic 0 and a light area to logic 1. The angular resolution will be:

$$\frac{360}{16} = 22{\cdot}5°.$$

With, say, 64 marks the resolution would be increased to:

$$\frac{360}{64} = 5{\cdot}625°.$$

Just one pulse per revolution of the shaft will be obtained from the reference sensor.

If the pulses from the main sensor are counted with a binary counter, then the binary count at any instant will be indicative of the angular position of the shaft. The basic idea is illustrated in Fig. 5.12. A Schmitt trigger is used to produce a fast changing edge to the pulse output of the main sensor regardless of the shaft speed and these are applied to the clock input of the binary counter. The system is initialised by turning the shaft until the reference sensor gives out a pulse. The reference pulse is used to clear the contents of the counter which is incremented by 1 for each pulse provided by the main track, thus keeping a record of the shaft position.

The bit-size of the counter will depend upon the number of revolutions of the shaft that need to be recorded, *e.g.* for 200 revolutions and 16 pulses per revolution the total number of pulses to be counted will be $200 \times 16 = 3200$, thus a 12-bit counter would be needed. The counter will thus keep a record

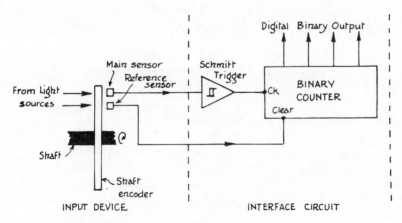

Fig. 5.12 Converting output of incremental shaft encoder into binary coded digital signal.

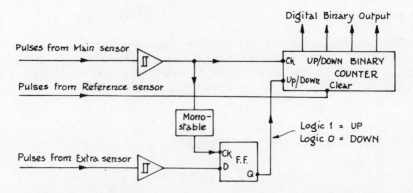

Fig. 5.13 System for forward/reverse operation of shaft.

of the number of revolutions as well as the angular position, with a resolution that can be adjusted by the fineness of the disc pattern. With some modification to the circuit arrangement, the rotational speed of the shaft may be obtained, *e.g.* by only allowing clocking of the counter during a known time interval (see Chapter 2 on use of counters).

In some applications it may be necessary to keep a record of the angular position of the shaft for forward or reverse rotation. This may be achieved by the use of an additional sensor, see Fig. 5.11(a), and an UP/DOWN counter. A basic arrangement is illustrated in Fig. 5.13.

During forward rotation of the shaft, the waveform outputs from the main and 'extra' sensor are as shown in Fig. 5.14(a) having a 90° phase relationship (θ). The monostable is triggered on the positive-going edges of the main

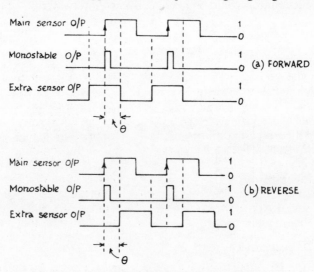

Fig. 5.14 Waveforms explaining operation of Fig. 5.13.

sensor pulses and its pulse output is supplied to the clock input of a D-type flip-flop. When the flip-flop is clocked, the D-input will be at logic 1 for forward rotation but at logic 0 for reverse rotation, see Fig. 5.14(b). Thus the Q output of the flip-flop may be used to place the counter in the UP or DOWN count modes, the digital output of which will be indicative of the angular position of the shaft after alternate forward and reverse movement.

Problem 1

An absolute shaft encoder disc consists of 7 concentric tracks with Gray code patterns. Determine:
a)   the angular resolution obtainable
b)   the Gray code output after the shaft has rotated through an angle of 25·3125° (assume 0° = 0000000)

Solution
a)   Angular resolution = $360/2^7$ = 2·8125°
b)   Decimal equivalent of Gray code = 25·3125/2·8125 = 9. Therefore Gray code = 0001101 (see Table 5.1).

Problem 2

An incremental shaft encoder produces 240 pulses from its main track per revolution of the shaft. Determine:
a)   the angular resolution
b)   the angular position of the shaft if the binary counter output is 1101.

Solution
a)   Angular resolution = 360/240 = 1·5°.
b)   The decimal equivalent of 1101 = 13. Therefore the angular position = 13 × 1·5° = 19·5°.

Keyboard Encoder

The keyboard used with a data communications terminal, professional/ home computer or control system consists of any array of labelled push-button switches (usually S.P.S.T.) A **keyboard encoder** is a digital device which generates a unique digital binary code when each key is operated; the coded output of the encoder usually conforming to a standard code such as the American Standard Code for Information Interchange (ASCII).

The basic principle of a keyboard encoder is illustrated in Fig. 5.15 using the ROM principle discussed in Chapter 3. When any key is operated, the diodes associated with that key conduct and the output bit line goes to +5V (logic 1). The absence of a diode will keep the bit line at 0V (logic 0). The logic states shown at the output of the bit lines conforms to ASCII coding when push-button A is operated.

In Theory, any number of push-buttons may be used, but in practice the number is limited to the number of connections that can be accommodated

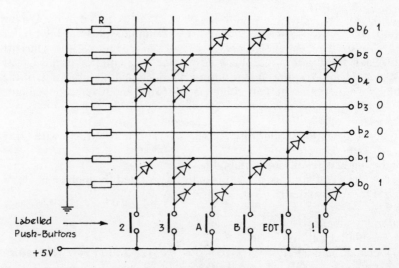

Fig. 5.15 Keyboard encoder (diode matrix ROM) showing binary coded output when key A is operated.

on the ROM i.c. package. For, say, 64 push-buttons the ROM would need 64 connections to generate the 64 different codes. The number of connections may be reduced by arranging the push-button switches in the form of a matrix.

Keyboard Matrix

An 8 × 8 keyboard matrix is shown in Fig. 5.16, where a push-button switch is placed at the intersection at each of the x and y lines (64 switches

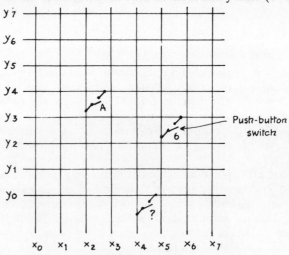

Fig. 5.16 8 × 8 key matrix (key switches placed at the 64 intersections of X and Y lines – but only a few shown here).

required). When key A is operated, line x_2 is connected to line y_4, similarly when key ? is operated line x_4 is connected to line y_0.

The x and y lines from the keyboard switch matrix are normally connected to the keyboard encoder as illustrated in Fig. 5.17. When an x and y line are connected together during push-button operation a unique address is

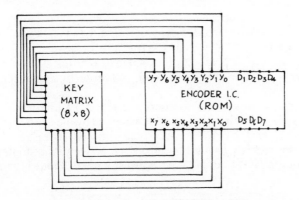

Fig. 5.17 Connection of key matrix to keyboard encoder.

provided for the ROM so that it outputs the code associated with the labelled push-button. The code appears on the D1-D7 pins of the encoder i.c. The number of connections to the encoder has now been reduced from 64 to 16. Note that the keyboard is an **input device** and the keyboard encoder an **interface circuit**.

Transistors, instead of diodes, may be used in the ROM and the basic idea is shown in Fig. 5.18 using multiple-emitter transistors connected as emitter-followers. When key A is depressed, TR2 conducts taking bit lines

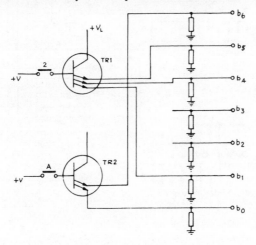

Fig. 5.18 Use of multi-emitter transistors to produce a keyboard encoding ROM.

b_0 and b_6 to the logic 1 state, all other lines remaining at logic 0. Similarly when key 2 is depressed, TR1 conducts and bit lines b_1, b_4 and b_5 are taken high, all other lines remaining at logic 0. In a non-matrixed arrangement with 64 push-buttons, 64 transistors would be required with 1 transistor having 6 emitters.

Scanned Keyboard Encoder

The basic keyboard encoder shown in Fig. 5.15 is a 'static' one, *i.e.* the addressing of the ROM remains static until a key is operated when a particular address is selected. Additional features must be incorporated into the encoder, such as switch debouncing and protection against multiple key operation.

In a 'scanning' keyboard encoder, see Fig. 5.19, the addressing of the ROM takes place continuously. This is achieved by the use of 2 ring-counters which are clocked by the clock oscillator (50–100kHz). The logic 1 circulating in each ring counter causes the sequential scanning of the 88 addresses of the ROM, and at each address a unique code is generated (the

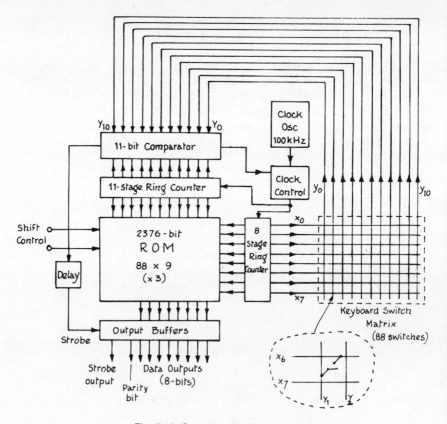

Fig. 5.19 Scanning keyboard encoder.

code does not appear at the data output of the encoder until the output buffers are 'enabled' or 'strobed').

When 1 of the keyboard switches is operated, 1 of the x outputs of the 8-stage ring counter is connected to 1 of the y inputs of the comparator. After a number of clock pulses a condition will occur where the circulating '1' applied to the comparator from the 11-stage ring counter will 'match' the circulating '1' applied to the comparator from the 8-stage ring counter via the closed keyboard switch. At the instant this occurs, a 'match' signal is applied to the clock control which inhibits the clock input to the 2 ring counters and the address scanning ceases. Only a single location in the memory is now addressed, particular to the key depressed. The 'match' signal from the comparator is also fed to the 'delay' circuit which acts as a common switch debouncer for all the keyboard switches. After a delay corresponding to the switch bouncing period (the delay is adjustable), a strobe signal is applied to the output buffers and the code from the ROM appears on the data output lines. When the depressed key is released, a 'match' no longer occurs in the comparator and the clock is re-applied to the two ring counters via the clock control causing the sequential scanning of the ROM addresses to re-commence.

The time elapsing from closing a keyboard switch to a match occurring will depend upon the clock frequency. If, for example the circulating logic 1 is in the first stage of both ring counters, the ROM address will be y_0, x_0. On each clock pulse the ROM addressing will move as illustrated by the diagonal lines of Fig. 5.20. The maximum time elapsing from closing any keyboard switch and a match occurring will be equal to 88 clock pulse periods. Thus

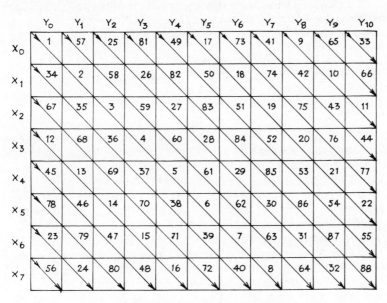

Fig. 5.20 Scanning cycle of encoder.

with a clock frequency of 100kHz the maximum time will be $88 \times 10\mu s = 0.88ms$. The actual time will depend upon the particular keyboard switch that is operated and the positions of the circulating 1s at the instant of switch closure.

At each addressed location there are actually three available 8-bit data codes. Which one that appears at the ROM output is determined by the **Shift** and **Control** keys on the keyboard. These keys, when depressed, apply a logic 1 to the appropriate shift and control input lines of the ROM. This facility allows a single key to be used for, say, upper or lower case A or a control character depending upon the logic state of the shift and control inputs.

Lock-out & Rollover

Scanning keyboard encoders are often said to provide **N-key Lock-out**. N-key or numerous-key lock-out operation means that if 2 or more keys are operated during 1 scanning cycle, the first down stroke that is detected will be the first to produce a match in the comparator and all other down strokes will be ignored (locked-out) until the first key is released.

In the **rollover** mode, keys that are depressed one after the other will be in the correct sequence provided each depression occurs in a different scanning cycle. **N-key Rollover** allows N-keys depressed in quick succession to be detected, *i.e.* **2-key Rollover** allows the detection of two keys operated in quick succession.

With N-key rollover it is necessary to make the key switches unidirectional. This is because if 3 keys are operated at the 3 corners of a square in the matrix, it will appear that the key in the fourth corner has been operated when it is scanned (phantom key operation). To make the switches unidirectional, diodes are placed in series with them.

OUTPUT DEVICES AND THEIR INTERFACING

Relay Driver

The output signal from a digital circuit may be used to operate an output device such as a relay or solenoid causing the closing or opening of relay contacts to initiate actions in other circuits or solenoid operation to initiate the on/off braking action of a rotating drum, for example.

If, say, a TTL gate is used in the buffer output of the digital circuit then it will only be capable of driving loads up to 10mA. If a relay or solenoid requires an operating current in excess of this figure, an **interface circuit** will be required as shown in Fig. 5.21.

When the output from the TTL gate is HIGH, TR1 is 'off' and so is TR2 thus the relay is de-energised. When the TTL gate output goes LOW, TR1 turns 'on' causing TR2 to turn 'on' and the relay to energise. TR1 and TR2 thus serve as current amplifiers increasing the sinking current output of the TTL gate from 10mA up to 250mA to operate the relay or solenoid. The diode D1 protects TR2 from over-voltage as TR2 switches-off, see Fig. 5.22.

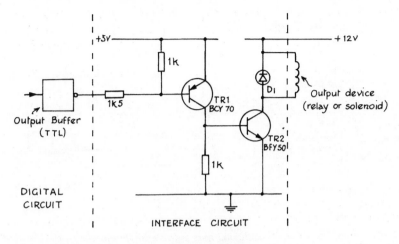

Fig. 5.21 Relay driver.

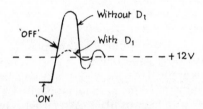

Fig. 5.22 Use of flywheel diode D1.

Alphanumeric Displays

Alphanumeric displays are commonly used as output devices in digital systems providing an indication of the measurement of such quantities as temperature, pressure, flow rate, vibration, time, frequency *etc* and for text display. Everyday examples include the displays on pocket calculators, video cassette recorders, digital watches and clocks, hand-held computers, hi-fi systems and washing machines *etc*.

Liquid crystal or l.e.d. displays may be employed using either 7-segment or dot matrix techniques. 7-segment displays were considered in Chapter 2 and Fig. 5.23 shows an arrangement for displaying the number of pulses counted which, for example, may give an indication of the frequency of a waveform or a measured time interval. B.C.D. counters are employed and these are interfaced to the 7-segment displays by 4-7 line decoders.

With this arrangement there are 28 bus lines to the display and four 4-7 line decoders are required. For a 6 digit display, 42 bus lines and six 4-7 line decoders are necessary. To produce economies in the number of decoders used and the number of lines to the display unit, **digital multiplexing** techniques may be employed.

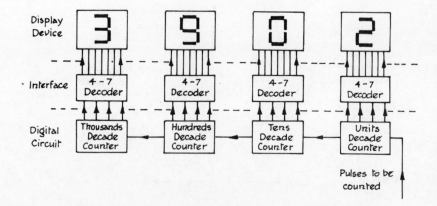

Fig. 5.23 Decade counters with decimal read-out.

Multiplexed Seven-Segment Display

An arrangement for a multiplexed display is given in Fig. 5.24 which requires the use of a shift register and a number of switch banks. At switch-on, +V is applied to C which initially appears across R, thus enabling via the parallel entry (PE) the parallel inputs P1-P4. P4 is loaded with logic 1 (+V) and P1–P3 with logic 0s (0V). After a short interval, corresponding to the time-constant CR secs, the PE terminal goes LOW and the clock pulses move the logic 1 sequentially through the shift register, connected as a ring counter.

The presence of a logic 1 at any of the Q1–Q4 outputs is used to close one of the switch banks A–D in sequence, thereby connecting a decade counter output to the 4-7 line decoder. The inverting buffers in turn provide logic 0 outputs to activate each display digit by taking the 'common cathodes' LOW.

It will be seen that each digit in turn is activated for a period of 1/200 secs. With 4 digits and a clock frequency of 200Hz, each digit will be activated at a rate of 200/4 = 50Hz. At this rate, due to persistence of vision, the display will appear as if it were continuously illuminated. This is **time-division multiplexing** of the display digits. With a 6 digit display a clock rate of 300Hz would be needed. There are now only 11 lines (7 + 4) to the display unit as opposed to 28 lines for the non-multiplexed system of Fig. 5.23 and only one 4-7 line decoder is required. Of course, switch banks and a shift register are required but the system still represents an economy in the electronic hardware.

An additional saving is made in the power consumed by the display. In a non-multiplexed system, each digit is continually illuminated whereas in a multiplexed arrangement each digit is illuminated in turn. The displays, of

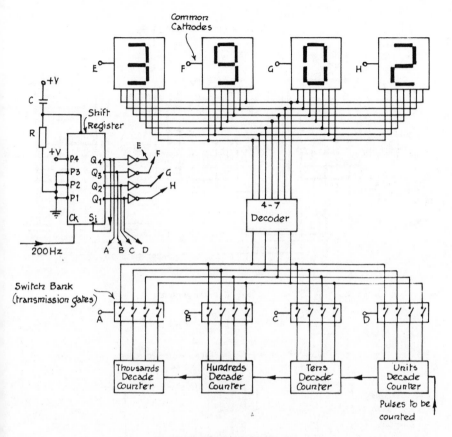

Fig. 5.24 Multiplexed display.

course, would be less bright but this can be improved by increasing the current drive to the l.e.ds and still maintain a saving in power consumed, which is important in battery operated systems.

Multiplexed Dot Matrix Display

An arrangement for a multiplexed l.e.d. dot matrix display is shown in Fig. 5.25(a). The i.c. is a 4 digit display (only 3 digits shown) with an integral shift register associated with each digit. The display digits are multiplexed on a column-by-column basis with common positioned columns illuminated together. Data is serial loaded into the shift registers and for 3 digits, 21-bits of data (1s or 0s) would be clocked into the serially connected registers for each of the 5 common columns, see Fig. 5.25(b). At the end of the 21 clock pulses (28 for a 4-digit display) a LOW (logic 0) is applied to the column 1 address line (C1), all other address lines remaining HIGH (logic 1).

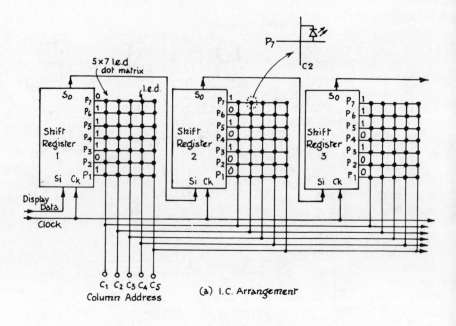

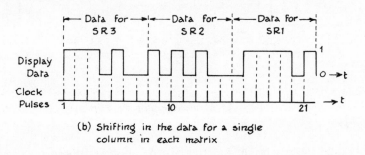

(a) I.C. Arrangement

(b) Shifting in the data for a single column in each matrix

Fig. 5.25 Multiplexed dot matrix display.

The parallel output data available from each register is then applied to the anodes of the l.e.ds. A HIGH state on an output line will cause an l.e.d. to illuminate and a LOW for it to remain extinguished for any of the l.e.ds in column 1. The logic states shown on the diagram represent the condition at the end of the clocking period for the data given in Fig. 5.25(b).

Fresh data for the common column 2 would then be clocked into the registers and a LOW applied to the C2 address line, all other address lines remaining HIGH, and so on. Eighty digit liquid crystal dot matrix displays are available in i.c. form which are capable of displaying the full ACSII character set and user defined symbols. The display may be under the control of an integral microprocessor and offer cursor facility.

Stepper Motor

Unlike a conventional motor, the shaft of a **stepper motor** does not rotate when power is switched-on; its shaft remains stationary until a **step pulse** is applied. The shaft then rotates through a precise angle and then stops until the next pulse is received. If step pulses are continually applied, the shaft will rotate continuously but in precise steps.

The **step angle** for the majority of stepper motors lies in the range of about 0·45° to 90°, *i.e.* between about 800 and 4 steps or pulses per revolution. For a given motor, the number of step pulses received will thus determine its rotational position *i.e.* With a step angle of 1·8°, a stepper motor, after receiving 20 step pulses will have rotated through an angle of $20 \times 1.8° = 36°$. The stepper motor may also be used for linear positioning as opposed to rotational positioning by using a lead screw and nut coupled to the motor shaft, see Fig. 5.26.

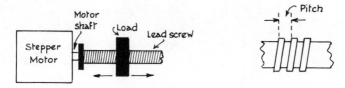

Fig. 5.26 Linear positioning.

Linear movement and number of step pulses are related by:

$$\text{Linear movement} = \frac{\text{No. of Step Pulses}}{\text{Steps per Revolution}} \times \text{Pitch of Leadscrew}$$

For example, if the pitch of the leadscrew is 0·4 inch/revolution and the motor step angle is 1·8°, the linear movement after 50 step pulses will be:

$$\frac{50}{200} \times 0.4 = 0.1 \text{ inches.}$$

Stepper motors are commonly used as **output devices** in digital systems for positioning applications in X-Y plotters, floppy disc head drives, automatic lathes, drilling machines *etc*. An important advantage of stepper motors in control systems is that because the speed and angular/linear positiong can be controlled by the step pulses, there is no need for 'feedback' sensors to monitor their performance, thus the control can be 'open-loop'. There are 3 main types of stepper motor: Variable Reluctance, Permanent Magnet and Hybrid. Two of these types will now be considered.

Variable Reluctance Stepper Motor

The motor consists of a soft iron rotor mounted inside a stator which has windings on its poles. The rotor and stator have a different number of poles or teeth and the example shown in Fig. 5.27 has 4 rotor poles, 6 stator poles

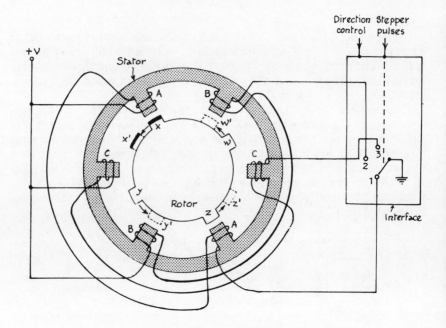

Fig. 5.27 3 phase variable reluctance stepper motor.

and 3 phases A, B and C. If phase A is energised with the switch in position 1, the rotor will take up a position of minimum reluctance aligning itself with the pole pieces of the stator on which phase windings A are wound.

When a step pulse is applied to the interface circuit, the switch takes up position 2, thus energising phase B. The rotor then moves so that its poles (shown dotted) align with the pole pieces on which phase windings B are wound. On the next step pulse, phase C will be energised and the rotor will step so that its pole pieces align with the stator poles on which phase windings C are wound. In this case one step is 30° but by increasing the number of poles or teeth, step angles as small as 1·8° can be achieved.

If instead of moving the switch in the order of positions 1-2-3, it is moved in the order 1-3-2 the direction of rotation can be reversed, this is the purpose of the 'direction control' input shown on the diagram. In practice the mechanical switch shown is replaced by switching transistors.

Permanent Magnet Stepper Motor

A permanent magnet stepper motor consists of a rotor which is magnetised with a number of poles and a stator with a number of windings on it. The arrangement shown in Fig. 5.28 utilise 4-phases A, B, C and D to produce a rotating magnetic field. With the switches in the position shown (1 and 3), phases A and C are energised and the permanent magnet rotor will

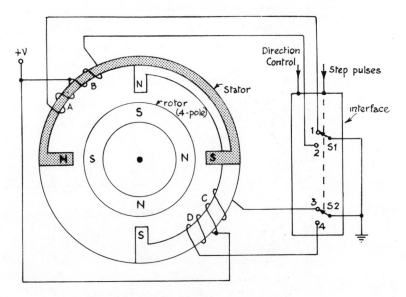

Fig. 5.28 Permanent magnet stepper motor.

be in the position shown. An incoming step pulse will cause the interface circuit to move S1 to position 2 but for S2 to remain in position 3 thus energising phases B and C. As a result the horizontal poles of the stator will reverse sign but the vertical poles will have their sign unchanged. The rotor will then take up the position as shown in Fig. 5.29, having rotated through a step angle of 90°. Table 5.2 shows the switch positions for continuous clockwise rotation.

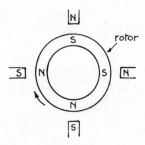

Fig. 5.29 Position of rotor for switch positions 2 and 3.

If the order of the switching in Table 5.2 is reversed, the direction of rotation will be reversed. By increasing the number of poles, stepping angles of 3·75° may be achieved.

Switch Positions	Rotor Angular Position
1 and 3	0°
2 and 3	90°
2 and 4	180°
1 and 4	270°
1 and 3	360°
2 and 3	90°
2 and 4	180°
etc	

Table 5.2 Relationship between switch position and angular position of the rotor.

Stepper Motor Drive

The simplest way to drive a single stator winding is as shown in Fig. 5.30(a) using a single transistor. When the transistor is turned 'on' by a step pulse, the supply voltage is just sufficient to produce the rated winding current. When the transistor is turned 'off', D1 (flywheel diode) provides a path so that current can decay without damaging the transistor, *i.e.* it reduces the amplitude of the voltage over-swing.

The circuit will operate satisfactorily as long as the interval between step pulses is not less than the L/R time of the winding, see Fig. 5.30(b). At higher step rates than this, the motor torque reduces because the rated current is never reached. The most common way of increasing the motor torque at

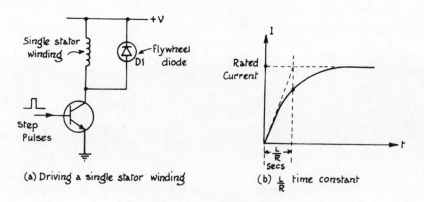

(a) Driving a single stator winding

(b) $\frac{L}{R}$ time constant

Fig. 5.30 Current forcing.

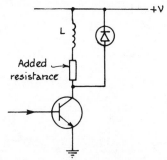

(c) Reducing the time-constant to improve current rise-time

Fig. 5.30 Current forcing.

high speeds is to add a resistor in series with each winding as in Fig. 5.30(c) so that the time constant is reduced.

Interfacing the Stepper Motor

A suitable interface circuit for a 4-phase permanent magnet stepper motor is given in Fig. 5.31. The mechanical switches of Fig. 5.28 at positions 1, 2, 3 and 4 are now replaced by the driving transistor pairs TR1/TR2, TR3/TR4, TR5/TR6 and TR7/TR8 respectively. The correct switching sequence for the drives to the stepper motor windings A, B, C and D is provided by a 'twisted ring counter', the outputs of which are used to switch the appropriate driver transistor pairs 'on' and 'off'.

To provide reverse rotation of the motor shaft, the ring counter outputs 1 and 2 are interchanged with outputs 3 and 4 respectively.

Servo Motor

There are many instances where the speed of a motor or the angular position of its shaft needs to be controlled accurately, *e.g.* speed control of a conveyer belt, head drum in a v.c.r. or a drilling machine or position control of a machine cutting tool. In these circumstances a 'servo' or control system is employed. When digital control of the motor is used, the servo motor forms the output device of the digital system.

A scheme for controlling the angular position of the shaft of an ordinary d.c. motor and hence the linear positioning of a load on a leadscrew is illustrated in Fig. 5.32. Two 'feedback' sensors are employed in the system; an incremental shaft encoder for angular positioning of the motor shaft and a tacho-generator for velocity control of the motor.

The system is initialised by moving the motor shaft until a reference pulse is produced (see description of incremental shaft encoder). The presence of a HIGH on the reference sensor output is used to (1) clear the contents of the up/down counter and (2) enable the clock oscillator. When the clock

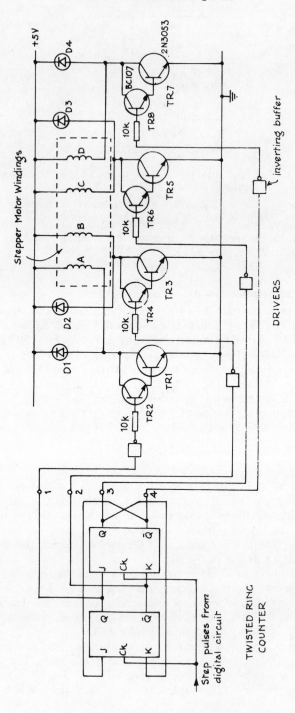

Fig. 5.31 Interfacing from digital circuit to stepper motor.

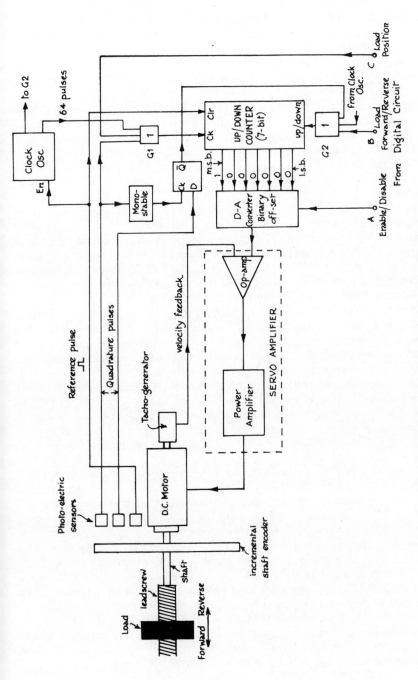

Fig. 5.32 Servo system for linear positioning of load (closed-loop).

oscillator is enabled, it applies a logic 1 to G2 which places the counter in the up-count mode. The clock oscillator then generates a sequence of 64 pulses which are applied to the clock input of the counter via G1. At the end of the 64 pulse sequence, the output of the counter will have the logic state shown in the diagram. This output is applied to a D–A converter operating in the binary off-set mode (see Chapter 4) but at this time it is disabled.

For forward rotation of the servo motor a logic 1 is applied to input B from the digital circuit which maintains the counter in the up-count mode. A number of pulses proportional to the desired load position is then applied to input C which causes the counter to count up from 1000000 to, say, 1000111. At the end of this period the logic 1 is removed from input B placing the counter in the down-count mode and a logic 1 applied to input A thus enabling the D–A converter.

The D–A converter then produces an output voltage of positive polarity of magnitude proportional to the binary input of 1000111. Note that 1000000 corresponds to 0V in binary off-set. The output voltage from the D–A converter is then applied to an OP-AMP connected as a difference amplifier. Since at this instant there is no output from the tacho generator, the voltage difference is large. The output from the OP-AMP is then applied to the power amplifier and the motor commences to turn.

As the shaft begins to turn, the tacho-generator gives out a d.c. voltage which is applied to the OP-AMP, reducing the difference voltage and slowing down the rate at which the motor shaft rotates. At the same time, the shaft encoder generates pulses which are applied to the counter which causes it to count down. As the binary counter counts down from 1000111 towards 1000000, the voltage output from the D–A converter reduces and less power is fed to the motor. When the count reaches 1000000, the output voltage from the D–A converter will be zero and the motor will stop with its shaft in an angular position proportional to the number of pulses(7) initially applied to input C. Hence the load will have moved in a forward direction from its reference setting.

If it is now desired to move the load in the reverse direction, a logic 0 is applied to input C placing the counter in the down count mode and a number of pulses applied to input C. The counter will then count down to, say, 0111100. When an enable is applied to the D–A converter, it will give out a voltage of negative polarity which will cause the motor to turn in the reverse direction. The change in direction is sensed by the D-type flip-flop which places the counter in the count up mode and the pulses produced by the shaft encoder will cause the counter to count back up to 1000000. When the count reaches 1000000, the motor will stop and the load will have moved to a new position in a reverse direction from its previous setting.

As can be seen a considerable amount of electronic hardware is required and quite complex control signals need to be generated by the digital circuit for this form of 'closed-loop' system, which should be compared with an equivalent arrangement using a stepper motor, illustrated in Fig. 5.33.

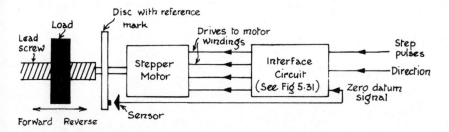

Fig. 5.33 Servo system for linear positioning of load using stepper motor (open-loop).

VOLTAGE LEVEL SHIFTERS

Sometimes it is necessary to alter the quiescent or active signal levels from one digital circuit so that it is suitable for application to another digital circuit, *e.g.* ECL to TTL and a voltage level shifter may be used for this purpose. An emitter-follower may be used as a simple voltage level shifter at the same time as serving as a buffer stage, see Fig. 5.34. In the

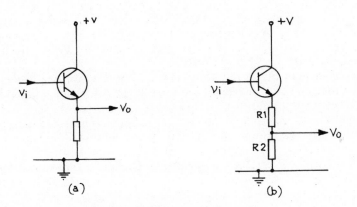

Fig. 5.34 Voltage level shifting.

arrangement shown in Fig. 5.34(a), the output voltage V is given by $V_0 = V_i - V_{be}$ (0·7V), which provides a voltage shift of 0·7V. If this voltage shift is not sufficient then the arrangement of Fig. 5.34(b) may be used. This increases the shift by the voltage dropped across R1. The disadvantage here is that the signal voltage suffers attenuation of:

$$\frac{R2}{R1 + R2}$$

To overcome the attentuation problem, the circuits of Fig. 5.35(a) or (b) may be used providing the slope resistance of the diodes in Fig. 5.35(a) or the

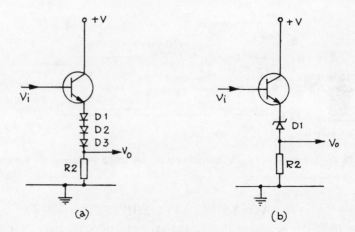

Fig. 5.35 Improved voltage level shifters.

zener diode in Fig. 5.35(b) is small compared with the resistance of R2. In Fig. 5.35(a) the output voltage is given by:

$$V_o = V_i - (V_{be} + V_{D1} + V_{D2} + V_{D3}) \fallingdotseq V_i - 2 \cdot 8V.$$

In Fig. 5.35(b) the output voltage is given by:

$$V_o = V_i - (V_{be} + V_z), \text{ } e.g. \text{ if } V_z = 6V, V_o = V_i - 6 \cdot 7V$$

The diagram of Fig. 5.36 shows how voltage level shifting using diodes may be used to shift the negative voltage levels associated with ECL into logic levels appropriate to TTL.

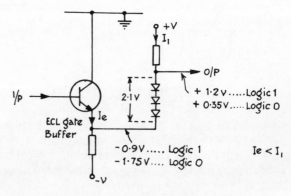

Fig. 5.36 Basic idea of voltage level shifting from ECL to TTL.

CHAPTER SIX

DISPLAY SYSTEMS

THIS CHAPTER IS concerned with the formation of characters on c.r.t. displays and the basic operation of visual display terminals. A schematic showing the essential stages of a visual display unit (V.D.U.) is given in Fig. 6.1 to which reference should be made with the descriptions that follow.

A V.D.U. consists of a keyboard, display c.r.t. and control electronics arranged in a single housing forming a 'video display terminal'. The terminal may be one of a number which permits the user to have 2-way communication via a 'private' or national data network using some form of digital transmission, or the terminal may 'stand alone'. The data link may be extensive over hundreds of miles, confined to a factory site or office block or limited to the distance between 2 adjoining rooms.

UNIVERSAL ASYNCHRONOUS RECEIVER–TRANSMITTER (U.A.R.T.)

Communication between one terminal and another usually takes place via a central computer using **serial data transmission**, whereas the V.D.U. is normally designed to process **parallel data**. The U.A.R.T. is used mainly for data transfers. It converts received serial data into parallel data which is in a suitable form for the V.D.U. to handle. When the terminal is sending or 'transmitting' messages to the central computer or to other terminals, the parallel data produced by the keyboard encoder (see Chapter 5) is converted into serial data by the U.A.R.T. for transmission over the communication link (serial data bus). The U.A.R.T. thus contains all of the necessary electronics for the parallel-to-serial and serial-to-parallel conversion; shift registers are commonly used for these purposes.

Asynchronous Data Transfer

With an asynchronous method of data transfer the time between the transmission of one character and the next is not fixed, *e.g.* the keys on the keyboard are depressed in a random fashion with no set time interval between operating one key and the next; the speed or data rate depends upon the typing speed of the operator. However, to be able to recognise

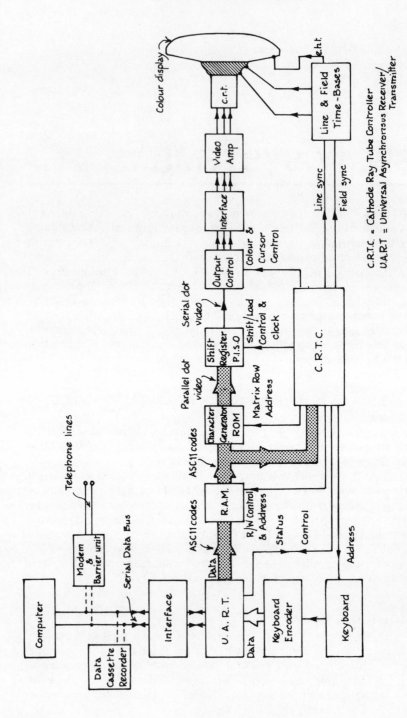

Fig. 6.1 The essential stages of a visual display unit (V.D.U.).

C.R.T.C. = Cathode Ray Tube Controller
U.A.R.T = Universal Asynchronous Receiver/Transmitter

each data bit of a transmitted character, the character block must be encoded so that the receiving station can detect exactly when the character block commences and thus pull into synchronism at the data bit rate. In asynchronous data transfer it is common to use 'start' and 'stop' bits for this purpose, see Fig. 6.2.

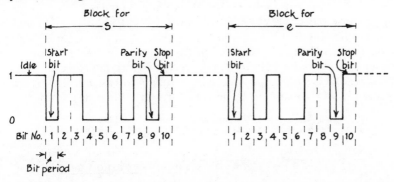

Fig. 6.2 Asynchronous data transfer.

In the absence of any transmission code, the input/output data line of the V.D.U. terminal rests in the HIGH or 'IDLE' state. To indicate when the transmission of a data byte is about to commence (particularly when the first bit is a logic 1) the start of any character is proceeded by a logic 0, the START bit, which acts as a timing reference. Immediately following the start bit is the 7-bit character code; a standard code such as the ASCII code (see Appendix E) or the EBCDIC code (Extended Binary Coded Decimal Interchange Code) is commonly used.

Bit 8 is used for 'parity checking' to provide some protection against transmission errors. Parity can be **odd** or **even** (even parity is used in Fig. 6.2). A character has odd parity if the total number of 1s (including the parity bit) add up to an odd number. Similarly a character has even parity if the total number of 1s (including the parity bit) add up to an even number. A few examples showing the required state of the parity bit for odd and even parity are given in Table 6.1.

| Bit 8 (Parity Bit) | | 7-bit Character Code |
Odd	Even	
1	0	0000000
0	1	1111010
1	0	1111000
0	1	1111111

Table 6.1 Odd and Even Parity

V.D.U. terminals connected to a communication network must be set to conform to the same parity specification. If any terminal receives a charcter that does not comply with the agreed standard, it is assumed that the charcter is in error. The idea is illustrated in Fig. 6.3 where even parity working is assumed. Fig. 6.3(a) shows the effect when a single bit (b_5) is inverted due to an error in the transmission path. At the receiving terminal, when an even parity check is carried out, an odd number of 1s will be detected indicating that the character is in error in which case it will not be displayed. The effect of 2-bits in error (b_3 and b_6) is shown in Fig. 6.3(b). When a parity check is carried out at the receiving terminal, an even number of 1s will be detected. Thus the receiving terminal will assume that **no errors** are present in which case an **incorrect** character will be displayed.

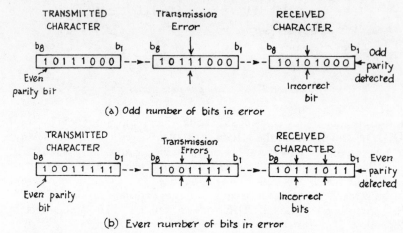

Fig. 6.3 Simple parity (even) operation.

It will therefore be appreciated that this simple method of 'error detection' only responds to changes in the state of an odd number of bits; changes in the state of an even number of bits will cause a false character to be displayed. To increase the number of detected errors, more sophisticated methods of error protection may be employed some of which will identify and correct the bit(s) in error (a facility not provided by the simple parity method used above).

Returning now to Fig. 6.2 it will be seen that each character byte is terminated with a STOP bit which ensures that the data line returns to the HIGH state ready for the transmission of the next character byte. Every asynchronous character block is encoded in this format.

U.A.R.T. Control Inputs

The U.A.R.T. is normally a dedicated large-scale integrated circuit formed on a single chip, see the block diagram of Fig. 6.4. It contains the

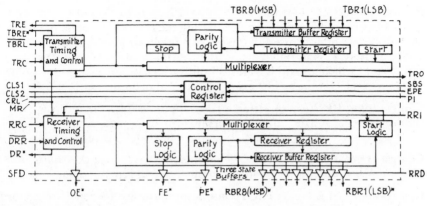

*These outputs are three state

Pin definition

Vcc	+ V supply
N/C	No Connection
GND	Ground
RRD	Receiver Register Disable
RBR₁₋₈	Receiver Buffer Register Outputs
PE	Parity Error
FE	Framing Error
OE	Overrun Error
SFD	Status Flags Disable
RRC	Receiver Register Clock
DRR	Data Received Reset
DR	Data Received
RRI	Receiver Register Input
MR	Master Reset
TBRE	Transmitter Buffer Register Empty
TBRL	Transmitter Buffer Register Load
TRE	Transmitter Register Empty
TRO	Transmitter Register Output
TBR₁₋₈	Transmitter Buffer Register Inputs
CRL	Control Register Load
PI	Parity Inhibit
SBS	Stop Bit Select
CLS₁,₂	Character Length Select
EPE	Even Parity Enable
TRC	Transmitter Register Clock

Pin connections

Vcc [1]	[40] TRC
N/C [2]	[39] EPE
GND [3]	[38] CLS₁
RRD [4]	[37] CLS₂
RBR₈ [5]	[36] SBS
RBR₇ [6]	[35] PI
RBR₆ [7]	[34] CRL
RBR₅ [8]	[33] TBR₈
RBR₄ [9]	[32] TBR₇
RBR₃ [10]	[31] TBR₆
RBR₂ [11]	[30] TBR₅
RBR₁ [12]	[29] TBR₄
PE [13]	[28] TBR₃
FE [14]	[27] TBR₂
OE [15]	[26] TBR₁
SFD [16]	[25] TRO
RRC [17]	[24] TRE
DRR [18]	[23] TBRL
DR [19]	[22] TBRE
RRI [20]	[21] MR

Fig. 6.4 RS6402 U.A.R.T.

necessary logic circuitry for carrying out the parity checks on the received data and during transmission is responsible for the insertion of the parity, start and stop bits into the data stream. Also, as previously mentioned, the U.A.R.T. provides serial-to-parallel and parallel-to-serial conversion of the received and transmitted data. In the system illustrated, conversion is effected using registers and multiplexer switches. The rate at which data is processed must be accurately maintained and this is normally achieved by the use of a crystal controlled oscillator. Clock pulse generation may be carried out in the U.A.R.T. i.c. and during the reception of data the 'start' and 'stop' bits may be used to enable and inhibit the local clock.

The U.A.R.T. is normally under the control of the 'Cathode Ray Tube Controller' which provides various control signals to enable or disable certain circuits within it. For example (see pin definition of Fig. 6.4).

Control Input RRD . . . A HIGH on this input disables the receiver SIPO shift register placing the output buffers in the high impedance state (tri-state buffers). Conversely, a LOW on this input will enable the receiver register.

Control Input $\overline{TBRL}$ . . . A LOW on this input will load the transmitter buffer register with parallel data when the terminal is in the sending mode.

Control Input EPE . . . A HIGH on this input causes the generation of an even parity bit during transmission or for the implementation of even parity checks on the data during reception. A LOW on this input will cause odd parity operation.

Due to the complex nature of the operations performed by the U.A.R.T. there may be 10 or more control inputs to it.

U.A.R.T. Status Flags

During the transmission or reception of data it is necessary for the C.R.T.C. to know exactly the state or 'status' of the U.A.R.T. during processing of the data. This is achieved by means of 'status flags', *i.e.* HIGHS or LOWS on particular output lines from the U.A.R.T. For example:

Status Flag TRE . . . A HIGH on this output indicates that the transmission of a character is completed including the stop bit, *i.e.* the transmitter register is empty.

Status Flag PE . . . A HIGH on this output indicates that the received character byte has failed the parity check.

Status Flag DR . . . A HIGH on this output indicates that the character has been correctly received and transfered to the receiver register buffer.

Data Inputs and Outputs

Apart from the control inputs and status flag outputs there will be received serial data in and parallel data out, also transmitted parallel data in and serial data out.

CATHODE RAY TUBE CONTROLLER (C.R.T.C.)

The C.R.T.C. acts as the 'systems controller' for the V.D.U. terminal and as such it must be capable of providing some measure of 'intelligent' action on the received or transmitted data. The degree of intelligence will depend upon the action required of the terminal in a particular data communication system and may vary from one manufacturer to another. In an 'Intelligent V.D.U. Terminal' it is not uncommon to find therefore that the C.R.T.C. is based on a microprocessor operating under a systems programme stored in ROM.

Apart from making decisions based on status flags received from the U.A.R.T. and taking action in the form of control signals to it, the C.R.T.C. is responsible for the generation of a number of timing signals to implement the orderly storage and display of the received ASCII characters as follows:

1) It must provide a read/write control input and address lines to the RAM. Normally, the received ASCII codes are stored in the RAM during the field flyback period and the codes are outputted from the RAM during the active field scan.
2) During the display period when the ASCII codes are fed to the ROM from the RAM, the C.R.T.C. must provide matrix row addresses to the ROM, a load/shift control and clock pulses to the ROM output shift register.
3) Operating on control codes received from the RAM, the C.R.T.C. will change the colour of the display via the output control block of Fig. 6.1. Also, when required, the C.R.T.C. is often responsible for the generation of the cursor.
4) It will generate timing pulses at line and field frequency for the synchronisation of the terminal timebases.

A simplified block schematic of a C.R.T.C. is given in Fig. 6.5. Further details of this timing section of the C.R.T.C. will be given later in the chapter.

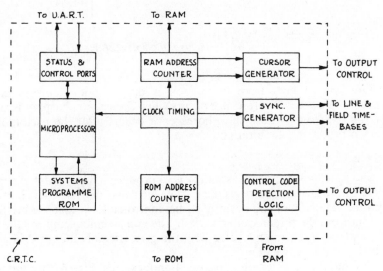

Fig. 6.5 Block schematic of C.R.T.C.

DISPLAY TUBES

Display tubes in current use in V.D.Us. are cathode ray tubes. These convert the serial dot video signals representing the alphanumeric and graphic symbols into light information patterns on the screen of the c.r.t. Monochrome or colour display tubes may be used and both types will be considered.

Monochrome C.R.T.

In a c.r.t. a beam of electrons is directed at high velocity towards a glass faceplate, the inside of which is coated with a layer of electroluminescent material that emits light on being struck by the electrons, see Fig. 6.6. This layer is called the screen phosphor and the colour of the light emitted depends upon the chemical composition of the layer. The light emitted from a 'monochrome' c.r.t. is usually white but phosphors may be chosen to produce green or blue displays.

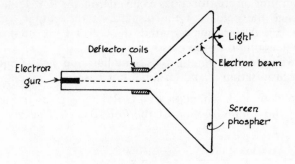

Fig. 6.6 Basic idea of display C.R.T.

Emission of light from the screen is due to both fluorescence and phosphorescence. Fluorescence occurs when the screen phosphor is excited by the electrons, whilst phosphorescence occurs after the excitation has ceased producing an 'afterglow'.

The Electron Gun

The function of the gun assembly is to produce a finely pointed beam of electrons to strike the c.r.t. screen. The electrons must have a high velocity and the intensity of the beam must be controllable so that the brightness output from the screen can be varied. The gun assembly employs the same principle as a thermionic valve with the gun assembly mounted in a glass envelope of high vacuum.

Common gun assemblies utilise 4-anodes, see Fig. 6.7(b) but other arrangements are possible. The production of the electron beam may be

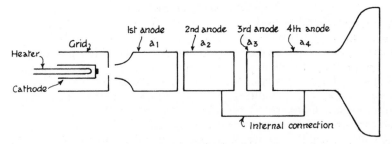

(a) 4-anode electrode assembly

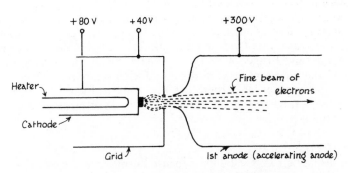

(b) Producing a fine beam of electrons

Fig. 6.7 The electron gun.

explained by considering Fig. 6.7(b). In a c.r.t. only a small beam current is
required and preferably the emission should come from a point source to
keep the beam dimensions small. In the gun structure shown, a small
cylindrical tube (the cathode) is coated with a small area of oxide emitter at
one end. A heater is passed down the centre of the tube and when fed with a
current raises the oxide emitter to a sufficiently high temperature for
emission to take place. To get the electrons moving towards the c.r.t. screen,
the first anode is placed at a potential of about 300–600V positive with
respect to the cathode. The resulting electric field that is set up between the
first anode and the cathode provides the initial acceleration of the electrons
on their way to the screen.

Surrounding the cathode is the control grid which consists of a cylinder
that is open at one end but has a fine aperture in it at the other end. Since the
grid is normally held at a potential which is negative with respect to the
cathode, the electric field set up between grid and cathode tends to return
the emitted electrons back towards the cathode. However, electrons of high
energy overcome the retarding field and converge on the grid aperture. On

entering the aperture the electrons come under the influence of the first anode potential and begin to accelerate and the resulting beam leaving the aperture is very narrow.

The intensity of the electron beam and hence the light output from the screen may be controlled by adjustment of the p.d. between grid and cathode. As the grid is made more negative to the cathode, fewer electrons reach the grid aperture resulting in a beam of lower intensity and a reduction in light output. Conversely, reducing the grid-to-cathode p.d. permits a greater number of electrons to reach the grid aperture resulting in a beam of higher intensity and a greater light output. If the grid is made sufficiently negative with respect to the cathode, none of the emitted electrons will reach the grid aperture. In consequence there will be no beam current and no light output from the screen.

When viewing a c.r.t. that emits white light, screen light of high intensity is interpreted as 'white', light of medium intensity as 'grey' and no light as 'black'. The actual colour of an unactivated screen appears a greyish colour, thus 'black' is the sensation of viewing the natural screen colour in contrast to the brighter energised areas. Although the beam leaving the grid aperture is very narrow, the electrons tend to diverge due to the natural repulsion they have for one another. It is therefore necessary to focus the beam in some way so that on arrival at the screen a sharply converging beam of electrons is obtained.

The Focusing Lens

In modern display c.r.ts. the beam is focused using an **electrostatic** lens. When an electron enters an electric field it tends to travel in a direction opposite to the lines of force, which by convention are shown existing from positive to negative sources of potential. Fig. 6.8 shows the basic action of a 3-anode electrostatic lens. The final anode potential (15–18kV) is supplied to a_2 and a_4; these anodes are commoned by an internal connection. A much

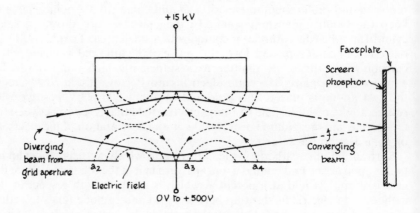

Fig. 6.8 An electrostatic lens.

lower potential (0–500V) is supplied to a_3 to set up the electrostatic fields as shown between the three anodes. Since electrons entering these fields tend to travel in paths exactly opposite to the lines of force, the diverging electrons will trace out curved paths causing them to become converging as they leave field of the focusing 'lens'. Once clear of the focusing field the electrons travel in straight line paths.

To ensure that the point of focus for the beam coincides with the screen phosphor, the contour of the electrostatic field may be altered by adjusting the potential supplied to the a_3 electrode. This potential is fed from the 'focus potentiometer' and a_3 is referred to as the 'focusing anode'.

The Viewing Area

When the electrons enter the focusing lens they decelerate whilst between a_2 and a_3 and then accelerate as they approach a_4. Once past a_4 the electrons coast along (but with high speed) since the screen phosphor coating is at the same potential as a_4. On arrival at the screen, the kinetic energy acquired by the electrons during motion is given up to the phosphor coating causing it to fluoresce.

The screen phosphor is deposited on the faceplate of the tube, see Fig. 6.9, which is made from heavy reinforced glass to protect the viewer from flying glass in the unlikely event of the tube imploding. In a 20″ tube the total

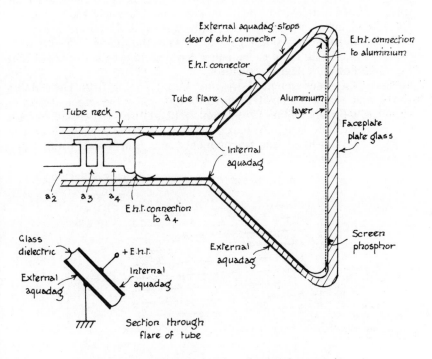

Fig. 6.9 Details of screen section of monochrome tube.

pressure on the faceplate is in the region of about 2300kg (1·5 tons) and extreme care should be exercised in handling a c.r.t. A careless blow may fracture the glass envelope and a serious implosion could result.

Deposited on the back of the screen phosphor is a very thin coating of aluminium. The aluminium serves as a highly reflective backing for the screen phosphor resulting in rearward light being reflected towards the viewer giving a greater light output from the tube. Additionally, the aluminised layer prevents 'ion burn' of the phosphor coating and provides a return path for electrons to the e.h.t. supply.

The inside and outside of the tube flare are coated with a layer of graphite (aquadag). The outer coating is normally connected to chassis and the inner coating is connected to the e.h.t supply and via spring clips to the second and fourth anodes. These 2 coatings separated by the thick glass of the tube form the e.h.t. supply reservoir capacitor (1750–2500pF). It is important to ensure that the tube capacitance is discharged before handling.

Producing a Raster

To be able to display text anywhere on the face of the c.r.t. screen, the electron beam must scan the whole of the screen area at high speed. It is thus necessary to deflect the electron beam simultaneously in both the horizontal and vertical directions.

The production of images on the screen of a c.r.t. is well established in the display of normal television pictures and not surprisingly the techniques employed are also used in V.D.Us. Indeed many V.D.Us are capable of accepting a normal television input signal. Thus the timing of the scanning electron beam inside the c.r.t. must be compatible for the display of data signals and normal television pictures.

In television a line sequential structure is used, see Fig. 6.10. The electron beam commences scanning at the top left-hand side of the screen and traces out line 1. At the end of line 1 the beam rapidly returns to the left-hand side and commences line scan 2. At the end of line scan 2, the beam again returns rapidly to the left-hand side to commence line scan 3 and so on. Upon

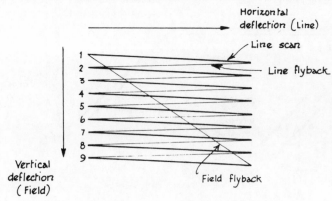

Fig. 6.10 Simple scanning producing a raster.

completing line scan 9 the electron beam rapidly returns to the top left-hand side of the screen to repeat the scanning process.

The movement of the electron beam from left-to-right constitutes what is known as the 'line scan' and the movement of the beam from top-to-bottom is known as the 'field scan'; the forces producing the deflection are derived from the respective line and field timebases. In order to give to the viewer the impression of a continuous flicker-free display, the complete scanning process from top-to-bottom of the screen must be repeated at least 50 times/sec.

Broadcast television does not use the simple scanning system depicted in Fig. 6.10 since a saving in signal bandwidth can be effected by employing an 'interlaced scanning' method, see Fig. 6.11. In an interlaced system and odd number of lines must be used and the diagram shows a 9 line interlaced system for simplicity by divided into two distinct fields with each field containing 4·5 lines. Scanning commences at A with the beam tracing out line scans 1, 2, 3 *etc* of the first field; it is the effect of the field scan that causes the line scans to be sloping. Half-way through line 5 the first field is completed and field 'flyback' commences at point B returning the beam to the top of the screen. If it is assumed that the field flyback is instantaneous, the other half of line scan 5 will be completed as shown when the second field commences at point C. Because of the 'half-line', scanning lines 6, 7, 8 and 9 of the second field now fit or 'interlace' between scan lines 1, 2, 3, and 4 *etc* of the first field.

At the end of line scan 9 the second field is completed and at D field flyback occurs once more returning the beam to the starting point A. This action is repeated over and over again at the 'picture rate' of 25 times/sec. Since each picture is composed of two interlaced fields, the **field time-base frequency is 50/Hz.**

In practice the television system used in this country employs 625 lines, thus each picture is composed of two interlaced fields with 312·5 lines in each field. Since the complete scanning process occurs 25 times/sec, **the line timebase frequency = 625 × 25 = 15625Hz.**

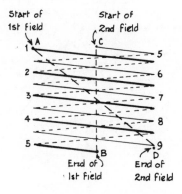

Fig. 6.11 Interlaced scanning (9-line system).

Deflecting the Electron Beam

Now that the line structure has been established, the means of deflecting the electron beam will be discussed. Display c.r.ts. in current use employ **magnetic** deflection and this is achieved by feeding the scanning currents into 2 sets of scan coils disposed at right angles to one another and fitted close to the tube neck, as illustrated in Fig. 6.12.

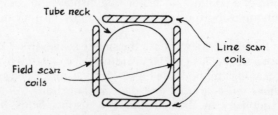

Tube neck

Line scan coils

Field scan coils

Fig. 6.12 Line and field scan coils.

When an electron enters a field of constant magnetic flux it experiences a force acting in a direction at right angles to both the direction of the field and the direction of motion of the electron beam, see Fig. 6.13. This force deflects the beam away from its original path with the result that the beam emerges along a path at an angle to its original direction. Whilst in the deflecting field, the electron travels in a curved path which is part of a circle of radius r. On leaving the deflecting field the beam travels in a straight line path. The magnitude of the angle through which the beam is deflected depends upon the strength of the magnetic field which for a given scan coil inductance, is dependent upon the magnitude of the scanning current supplied to the scan coils.

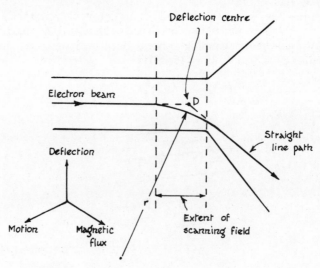

Fig. 6.13 Deflecting the beam (magnetic deflection).

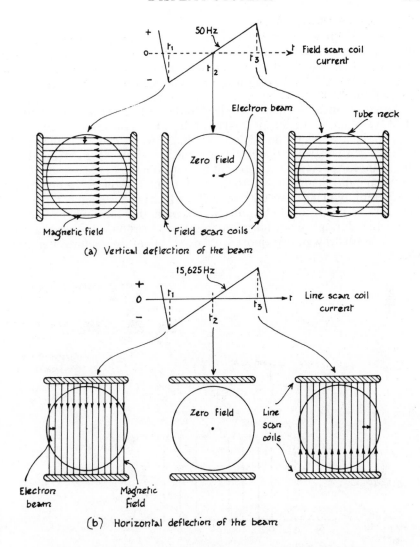

Fig. 6.14 Diagrams showing magnetic fields set up by scanning currents.

The diagram of Fig. 6.14 show the magnetic fields set up by the scanning currents supplied to the field and line scan coils. The direction of the resulting force acting on the beam may be found by applying Fleming's Left-Hand Rule, but note that electron motion is opposite to conventional current flow. In both diagrams the electron beam is assumed to be moving out of the paper. Quite clearly, in order to produce deflection left or right and up or down from the screen centre, the line and field scanning currents must be a.c. type waveforms.

Modulating the Beam Current

To produce alphanumeric or graphic images in the screen of the display tube, the beam current must be turned 'on' and 'off' in accordance with the 'dot video' signal supplied from the video amplifier during the line scanning process. This is achieved by allowing the video signal to alter the bias voltage between the grid and cathode of the electron gun.

The video signal is usually supplied to the cathode of the c.r.t. and the effect that it has on the beam current of the c.r.t. is illustrated in Fig. 6.15. With no signal applied, the brightness voltage (which may be applied to the grid of the c.r.t.) is set so that the cut-off voltage point is reached resulting in zero beam current and hence no light output from the c.r.t. Each sequential dot video pulse that is applied to the c.r.t. cathode reduces the bias on the gun thereby allowing beam current to flow which produces light output from the c.r.t. screen. It should be noted at this point that the modulation of the c.r.t. beam during a single line scan produces a 'part only' of each character in a horizontal row of text; more will be said about this feature later in the chapter.

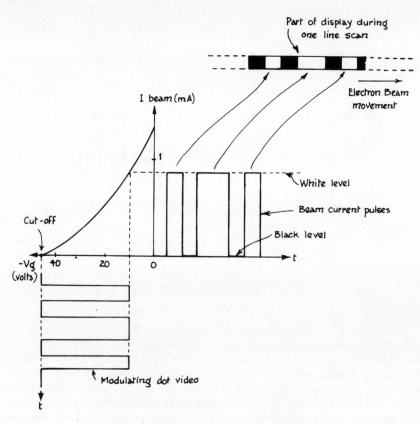

Fig. 6.15 Modulating the beam current.

Centralising the Raster (Picture shift)

Some means must be provided to centralise the raster on the screen due to positional errors in the alignment of the gun assembly in the neck of the c.r.t. and manufacturing tolerances in the scan coil assembly. With a monochrome c.r.t. picture shift is normally achieved by applying weak magnetic fields from permanent magnets fitted on the outside of the tube neck. Commonly the magnets are in the form of magnetised annular rings as shown in Fig. 6.16(a). The rings are magnetised in such a way as to set up a magnetic field across the tube neck. Two rings are used which can be rotated independently of one another as in Fig. 6.16(b).

The resultant magnetic field of the 2 rings can be moved radially by moving the rings together in the same direction and the strength of the field may be adjusted by moving the rings in opposite directions. Movement of the rings thus allows the electron beam to be deflected in any radial direction by a controlled amount causing an appropriate shift in the raster on the screen. The shift magnets are mounted immediately behind the scan coil assembly, see Fig. 6.16(c) and so correct the beam position prior to it being deflected by the scanning fields.

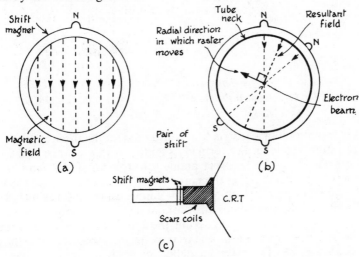

Fig. 6.16 Picture shift.

Colour C.R.T.

Many of the principles and features described for the monochrome c.r.t. are used in colour display tubes. They employ similar beam forming principles and use **electrostatic focusing** and **magnetic deflection** of the electron beam. Colour tubes, however, differ because of the need to provide 3 electron guns with each gun associated with a light emitting phosphor of a different colour and the precision with which the guns must be aligned and their electron beams controlled to produce unblemished colour images.

In-Line Colour Tube

The in-line gun colour tube is the most important colour display c.r.t. used in visual display terminals. A diagram showing the basic principle of a 'precision in-line' tube is given in Fig. 6.17.

The 3 electron guns are arranged in a horizontal line and employ electrically separate cathodes. The control grids of each gun, however, are joined together as they are formed from a single piece of metal. Separate heaters provide electron emission from the 3 cathodes and a variable voltage may be applied to the commoned grids for brightness control purposes (similar to that for a monochrome tube).

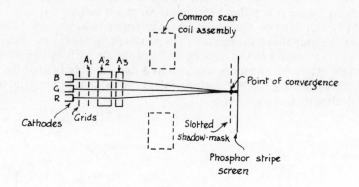

Fig. 6.17 Basic principle of precision in-line (PIL) colour C.R.T.

A one-piece metal construction is also used for the three anodes. A_1 is the accelerating anode and is normally supplied with a voltage in the range of 500–1000V, A_2 is the focusing anode (electrostatic focus) and is supplied with a voltage that is higher than in a monochrome tube of about 5kV and A_3 is the final anode to which the e.h.t. supply at about 24kV is fed.

The three electron beams start off parallel to one another but the outer beams are bent slightly by off-setting the apertures in the final anode so that the beams cross-over one another (converge) at a single point in the **plane of the shadow-mask**. The magnetic deflecting fields set-up by the line and field scan coil assembly operate on all 3 beams and the design is such that during deflection the point of convergence is maintained in the plane of the shadow-mask.

Shadow-Mask and Screen

The screens of colour tubes use phosphors that emit light in the red, green and blue parts of the colour spectrum. The particular wavelengths of the red, green and blue light radiations are chosen so that by mixing the 3 colours in suitable proportions a very wide range of colours may be produced; a significant consideration in the production of normal colour television images.

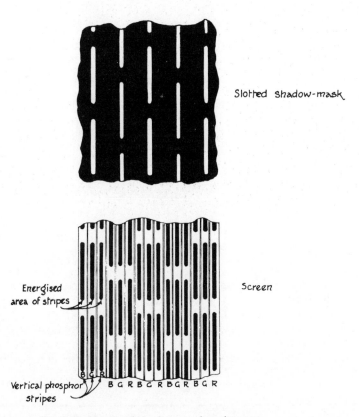

Slotted shadow-mask

Screen

Energised
area of stripes

Vertical phosphor   B G R B G R B G R B G R
stripes

Fig. 6.18 Details of shadow mask and screen.

With in-line tubes the screen phosphors are laid in the form of vertical
stripes as shown in Fig. 6.18 and each electron beam is associated with a
particular coloured stripe. The steel shadow-mask is slotted with the slots
bridged at regular intervals to accommodate the spherical contour shape
required by the mask. When the 3 beams cross over one another in the plane
of the mask, the portion of each beam passing through the slots falls on its
respective coloured stripes.

The purpose of the shadow-mask may be understood by considering
Fig. 6.19 which shows the 3 electron beams, in a plan view, arriving at a
single position on the screen. It will be seen that the part of the green beam
passing through the slots in the mask fall on the green phosphor stripes, *i.e.*
the mask 'shadows' the green beam from the blue and red phosphor stripes.
Similarly, the mask allows the red and blue beams to strike only their
respective coloured stripes. Because the 'beam landing areas' on each stripe
are very small, the eye does not perceive the individual areas but only the
additive mixture of their light outputs; this is the essential underlying
principle of colour display tubes.

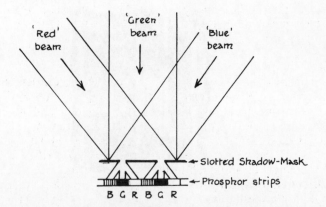

Fig. 6.19 Diagram showing action of shadow-mask.

Display Colour

In a V.D.U. alphanumeric or graphic symbols may be displayed in any of the following colours: RED, GREEN, BLUE, YELLOW, CYAN, MAGNENTA and WHITE by switching 'on' or 'off' the appropriate guns. When two or more guns are switched 'on', the colour that is seen by an observer is the result of 'additive mixing' of the coloured light outputs from the individual phosphors. The conducting state of the guns for the 7 colours mentioned is given in Table 6.2.

Screen Colour	Gun State
RED	Red gun 'on'. Blue and Green guns 'off'
GREEN	Green gun 'on'. Blue and Red guns 'off'
BLUE	Blue gun 'on'. Red and Green guns 'off'
YELLOW	Red and Green guns 'on'. Blue gun 'off'
CYAN	Blue and Green guns 'on'. Red gun 'off'
MAGENTA	Red and Blue guns 'on'. Green gun 'off'
WHITE	Red, Green and Blue guns 'on'
BLACK	Red, Green and Blue guns 'off'

Table 6.2. Conducting state of electron guns

The range of colours that are available for alphanumeric and graphic displays is more limited than for normal colour television displays because with the former the video drive signals are, of course, digital but with the latter they are analogue. It is possible to display text in colours, other than those given, by altering the amplitude of the digital drive signals to a particular gun(s). For example to produce orange text, the digital drive to the red gun would need to be about twice the amplitude of the drive to the green gun.

Purity

The **purity** of a raster depends upon how accurately the 3 beams land on their respective phosphor stripes. If each gun is switched-on in turn, pure red, green and blue rasters should be obtained and if all 3 guns are switched-on, a pure white raster should be achieved. Purity errors are caused by beams striking incorrect colour phosphors and show up as 'patches' of the wrong colour. These errors arise when a beam has an incorrect angle of approach to the deflecting fields.

Correction for wrong approach to the scanning fields is carried out by a pair of purity rings mounted on the tube neck. The purity rings are annular magnets and are similar to the picture shift magnets used with monochrome tubes. The provide a magnetic field across the tube neck that can be varied in strength and moved in any radial direction by altering the relative positions of the two magnets. The location of the rings is shown in Fig. 6.22.

Purity errors are also caused by stray magnetic fields in the vicinity of the colour tube which induce magnetism into the steel shadow-mask or tube supports. To take care of accidental magnetism which may occur if a vacuum cleaner or electric drill is brought close to the tube, display terminals are fitted with **automatic degaussing coils** which are brought into operation each time the terminal is switched 'on'. A common degaussing circuit is given in Fig. 6.20

The automatic degaussing coils are fitted on a mild steel magnetic shield surrounding the cone of the tube and are disposed at the top and bottom of the tube cone. Each coil is arranged so that it is partly outside and partly inside the magnetic shield and that the influence of its magnetic field extends to the shadow-mask, tube rim band and tube supports.

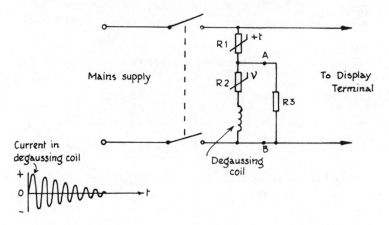

Fig. 6.20 Auto-degaussing circuit.

R1 is a thermistor with a positive temperature coefficient, R2 is a voltage dependent resistor and R3 an ordinary linear resistor. At switch-on, R1 is of low resistance and a large voltage is developed across A – B. With a large voltage applied to R2 its resistance will be low and thus a large current will flow in the degaussing coil. This current must be sufficient to magnetically saturate the shadow-mask, rim band and tube supports. As R1 heats up, its resistance increases and the voltage across A – B falls causing the resistance of R2 to increase. Thus the current in the degaussing coil will gradually decrease as shown, taking the components to be degaussed through many cycles of diminishing magnetisation. The current in the shunt resistor R3 maintains R1 'hot'.

Static Convergence

In the absence of the deflecting fields, *i.e.* when the beams are at the centre of the screen as in Fig, 6.17, the three beams must cross-over one another or 'converge' in the plane of the shadow-mask. If this does not occur there will be colour 'fringing'. To take care of manufacturing tolerances, say, in the positioning of the apertures in the final anodes of the electron guns, it is usual to provide some means of adjustment to set the convergence at the screen centre (static convergence).

In a precision in-line tube the static convergence may be accurately set with the aid of two pairs of barium ferrite ring magnets fitted on the tube neck. One pair is magnetised to give 4-pole fields as in Fig. 6.21(a) and the other pair gives 6-pole fields as in Fig. 6.21(b). The 4-pole fields move the

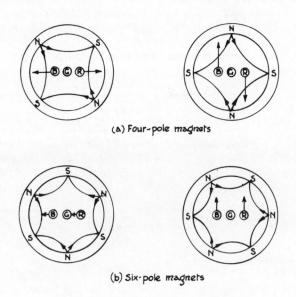

(a) Four-pole magnets

(b) Six-pole magnets

Fig. 6.21 Static convergence magnets.

outer beams in opposite horizontal and vertical directions whilst the 6-pole fields move the outer beams in the same horizontal and vertical directions. Thus by adjustment of ring magnets, the blue and red beams can be made to converge with the green beam at the screen centre. The disposition of the static convergence magnets are given in Fig. 6.22.

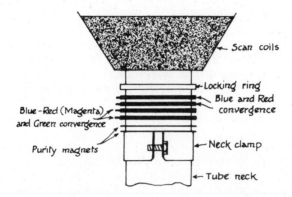

Fig. 6.22 Location of purity and static convergence magnets.

With the Mullard 30AX in-line tube, the external static convergence assembly and the purity magnets are replaced by a single thin magnetic wire ring incorporated in the gun assembly. This ring is magnetised with 2, 4, and 6 pole fields of the required strength and direction during manufacture so that no further purity or static adjustments are necessary.

Dynamic Convergence

Without any compensation, convergence will not be maintained out to the edges of the screen since the beams are deflected through an arc and the screen has a large radius of curvature, *i.e.* is nearly flat. During deflection the beams will cross over behind the mask and become divergent upon reaching it.

The problem of dynamic convergence for in-line tubes has been solved in an ingenious way, and for screen sizes up to 19″ there are no extra adjustments to the static ones. The **self-converging action of the in-line tube** depends primarily upon the use of astigmatic or non-linear deflecting fields, (For details of dynamic convergence theory for in-line tubes and further information on colour display tubes, see *Colour & Mono Television Vol 2* by K.J. Bohlman, published by Dickson Price.) the theory of which is outside the scope of this introduction to V.D.Us. The required non-linear field distribution is achieved by employing a special deflection coil assembly known as a 'precision static toroid'. Each turn of wire is precisely placed in winding grooves on plastic rings attached to each end of the deflection assembly. By this means a tightly controlled field distribution with the right amount of astigmatism is obtained.

Picture Shift

The picture shift magnets associated with monochrome c.r.ts. are not used with colour display tubes as their magnetic fields would upset purity and convergence. For this reason, picture shift for colour display tubes is carried out by passing direct currents through the deflection coils. The currents are set by d.c. shift controls in the line and field time-bases for correct centring of the raster.

CONVERTING THE ROM OUTPUT INTO SERIAL FORM

To produce characters on the screen·of the display tube using a line sequential system, the parallel data output of the ROM must be converted into serial form.

Character Matrix

The video signal which produces the display characters consists of a series of digital pulses. For a monochrome display, each pulse corresponds to an element of white (or black) on the screen. A character is thus constructed from a series of dots on the screen. Since each dot area is equal to the size of the scanning electron beam, the number used for each character will determine the size of the character on the screen. If too many dots are used the amount of text that can be fitted into the screen area will be limited. On the other hand if too few are used, the characters may not be discernable from a normal viewing distance. All normal alphanumeric and graphic shapes are therefore arranged to fit into a standard size dot matrix, see Fig. 6.23.

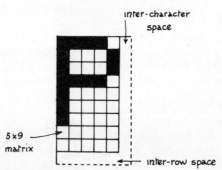

Fig. 6.23 5 × 9 character matrix.

The matrix is commonly 5 × 9 and as each dot occupies the width of the scanning beam, the dot matrix is 9 scan lines in height. When text is written onto the screen, inter-character and inter-row spacing must be provided. Thus the display dot matrix is effectively 6 × 10 and the display electronics is arranged to handle this format, where column 6 and row 10 are always blank.

Display Format

A typical display format, see Fig. 6.24, consists of 24 rows of characters with up to 40 characters per row. The rows of characters may occupy the full width of the screen or a margin may be used around the display area as shown. Out of the 52μs available for the active line scan, 40μs from each line scan may be chosen to display text thereby allowing 6μs wide margins on each side of the screen. Thus each of the 40 displayed characters is allocated a time slot of 1μs. Thus each dot period is of ⅙ μs duration.

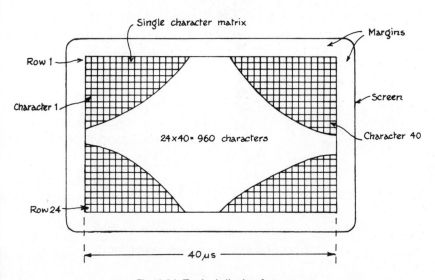

Fig. 6.24 Typical display format.

The margins at the top and bottom represent about 10% of the total screen height resulting in about 480 lines being used for the display of characters.

Effect of Interlaced Scanning

Since each displayed picture is composed of two interlaced fields, every dot matrix row for any character is repeated twice in each text picture period. Thus in practice, **normal sized characters are 20 line scans in height** which includes 2 scan lines for inter-row spacing. An example is given in Fig. 6.25 showing the display of the upper case letter P.

ROM output Shift Register

The use of a ROM as a character generator was discussed in Chapter 3. To convert the parallel data words appearing at its output into serial form, a P.I.S.O. shift register is used, see Fig. 6.26. Each 5-bit parallel data word corresponding to each matrix row of the character to be displayed is loaded

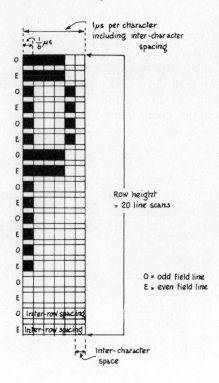

Fig. 6.25 Effect of interlaced scanning.

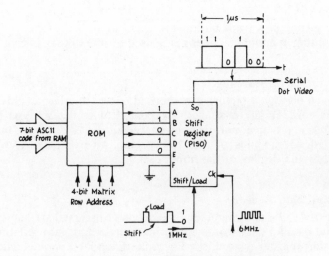

Fig. 6.26 Converting the ROM output into serial form.

into the shift register by applying a HIGH to the shift/load input of the register at a rate of 1MHz. To provide the inter-character space, bit F is permanently 'hard wired' to logic 0. When the 1MHz pulse ends, the shift/load line goes LOW which places the register in the shift mode. The 6-bit data word is then clocked out from the register in serial form by the 6MHz pulses applied to the clock input.

When the next matrix row of the character is addressed another 5-bit data word will be applied to the shift register from the ROM. This will be loaded into the register on the next 1MHz pulse (HIGH) applied to the shift/load input. The 6-bit data word will be clocked out in serial form when the shift/load line goes LOW at the end of the 1MHz pulse. This continues until all of the matrix rows have been clocked out in serial form.

It should be noted that after each data word has been clocked out of the register, it will hold only logic 0s. This permits the margins to be produced by

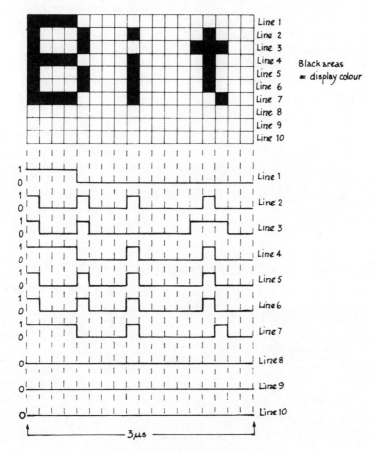

Fig. 6.27 Dot video signal required to produce three consecutive characters in a row of text.

only allowing the 1MHz pulses to be applied to the shift register during specific time intervals. The diagram of Fig. 6.27 shows the dot video waveforms produced by the shift register when displaying 3 consecutive characters in a row of text. Note that for any row of displayed characters, matrix row 1 is outputted from the ROM for **all of the characters in the row**, followed by matrix row 2 and matrix row 3 *etc*.

If the video waveforms are fed to the cathode of a monochrome display tube on consecutive line scans with the correct polarity, white text on a black background would be produced (or black text on a white background with opposite polarity).

Colour Display

An arrangement for supplying dot video signals to the 3 guns of a colour display tube is given in Fig. 6.28. It is, of course, necessary for the terminal to 'know' what colour the intended display of text is to be. This information is provided by the transmission source by using some of the ASCII codes for colour control purposes. Examples are given in the table of Fig. 6.28 where it will noted that the logic state of $b_1 - b_3$ determine the display colour. Also it is necessary for the terminal to 'know' whether or not the received code is a control code, since control codes are displayed as blanks on the screen. It

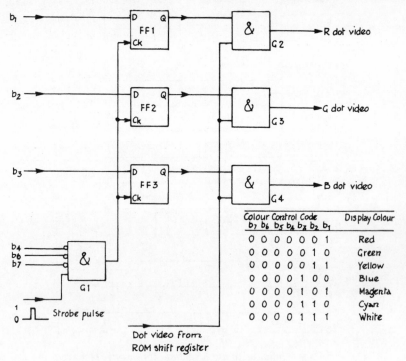

Colour Control Code							Display Colour
b_7	b_6	b_5	b_4	b_3	b_2	b_1	
0	0	0	0	0	0	1	Red
0	0	0	0	0	1	0	Green
0	0	0	0	0	1	1	Yellow
0	0	0	0	1	0	0	Blue
0	0	0	0	1	0	1	Magenta
0	0	0	0	1	1	0	Cyan
0	0	0	0	1	1	1	White

Fig. 6.28 Controlling the display colour.

will be seen that b_4, b_6 and b_7 of a colour control code are always at logic 0. This information may be used to produce the blanks on the screen and to initiate the switching of the display colour.

When a colour control code is encountered, bits 4, 6 and 7 will be at logic 0. Thus if a strobe pulse is applied to G1, a logic 1 will appear at this gate output to be fed as a clock pulse to the 3 flip-flop latches. As a result the Q output of the flip-flops will be set at the logic state of their respective inputs. (b_1, b_2 and b_3).

Suppose that bits 1 and 2 are at logic 1 and bit 3 is at logic 0. this will cause the AND gates and G2 and G3 to be operative but for G4 to be inoperative. Thus the input dot video from the ROM shift register will appear at G2 and G3 outputs to produce yellow text on the screen.

Display Timing

The schematic diagram of Fig. 6.29 shows the timing section of the C.R.T.C. that is necessary to produce the video display. Received ASCII codes from the U.A.R.T. are stored in the RAM during the field flyback period by making the R/W line LOW. During display, *i.e.* the active field period, this line is taken HIGH placing the RAM in the read mode. The

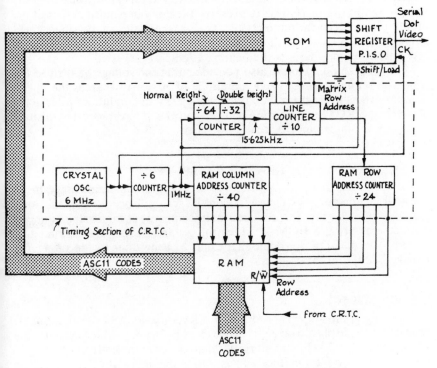

Fig. 6.29 Block schematic of timing section of C.R.T.C.

ASCII codes are then fed to the ROM where they provide the address, selecting in sequence the stored characters.

Timing is controlled by a stable 6MHz crystal oscillator which after division provides row and column addresses for the RAM and matrix row address for the ROM. A 6MHz output from the oscillator is supplied as a clock input to the ROM output shift register and after division-by-six, 1MHz pulses to the shift/load input of the shift register.

For normal height characters, the ROM matrix row address is incremented by 1 for each line scan. To obtain **double height** characters, the ROM matrix row address only needs to be incremented by 1 for **every 2 line scans**. This will cause the same matrix row of the character to be repeated on a pair of consecutive line scans. Thus the character will be 40 line scans (with interlacing) in height as opposed to 20 line scans for normal height characters. The detection of the **double height control character** may be used to change the division of the ÷ 64 counter to ÷ 32 operation.

Video Amplifier Requirements

The pulse output of the ROM shift register is of a very sharp nature having rise and fall times of the order of 10ns. To produce well defined text on the screen, the video amplifier stages will normally have a bandwidth extending from zero up to 15 or 20MHz to preserve the dot video pulse output of the shift register. Special attention is also given in the design of the video stages to ensure that the rise and fall times are similar so that the lagging edge of text images are as sharp as the leading edge.

The video amplifier must also provide sufficient voltage gain since the c.r.t. will require a pulse drive amplitude of 50–150V whereas the digital output of the shift register may only be, say, 5V in amplitude. Interfacing between the ROM output shift register and the video stages may also be necessary for impedance matching.

GRAPHICS DISPLAY

The use of graphics permits the construction of low definition diagrams or extra large alphanumeric characters on the screen. The video signals for a graphics character may be produced in the same way as for an alphanumeric character by using a ROM in which the graphic shapes are permanently stored. Alternatively, a graphic shape may be generating by 'decoding' the received ASCII graphic code.

Graphics Matrix

When a graphic shape is produced by 'decoding' its ASCII code, graphic characters are displayed on a 2 × 3 matrix as in Fig. 6.30 which occupies the whole of the 6 × 10 alphanumeric dot matrix. Since the matrix consists of 6 segments, the simplest method of generating the required video signal is to allocate 1-bit of the received ASCII code to each of the segments. When a

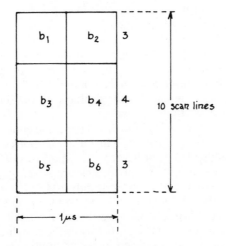

Fig. 6.30 Graphics matrix.

data bit is at logic 1 the corresponding segment is illuminated, but if at logic 0 it is left dark. Only 6 of the bits from each graphics code are used to identify the state of the segments.

Graphic symbols are normally displayed with the segments of the matrix touching one another; these are referred to as 'contiguous' graphics. Each graphic symbol may also be displayed in the 'separated' graphics form where the size of the illuminated areas are reduced so that they do not touch one another. Examples of both display forms are given in Fig. 6.31 for one of the standard graphic symbols. The use of separated graphics gives greater flexibility in the design of display pages.

It will be noted from Fig. 6.30 that the 10 scan lines per field allocated to a graphic symbol must be split into 3 groups. Since the 10 scan lines cannot be split into equal groups, the format of 3–4–3 is adopted which in practice is found to be acceptable.

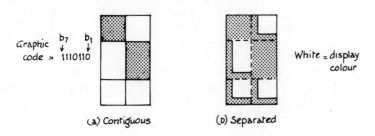

Fig. 6.31 Graphic symbol forms.

Graphics Generator

The production of the serial video data signal for a graphics symbol is performed in exactly the same way as for an alphanumeric symbol. Since a graphic symbol is 6 dots wide, then the parallel-to-serial conversion shift register will also have 6 inputs. With contiguous graphics there are no inter-symbol or inter-row spaces, hence bit F may be at logic 1 or logic 0 depending upon the particular graphic symbol. Similarly the tenth scan line will not necessarily be 'blank'.

One way of 'decoding' the ASCII graphic codes to produce the inputs to the shift register is illustrated in Fig. 6.32 A 4-bit binary counter which is reset at the end of the tenth line scan of each row of text is used to identify the scan line in the graphics matrix. The output of this divide-by-ten counter is fed to a 4-to-16 line decoder, but only 10 of the outputs are used (y_0 to y_9). For each of the 10 scan lines a logic 0 appears on one of the decoder output lines (all other output lines being at logic 1). It will be noted that the decoder outputs are grouped in the same way as the scan lines in the graphics matrix, *i.e.* in a 3–4–3 format. Each group is applied to the inputs of the gates G1–G3. Because of the grouping only one of the NAND gates will give out a logic 1 on each scan line. Note that G1 produces an output of logic 1 for the first 3 scan lines, G2 for the next 4 scan lines and G3 for the last 3 scan lines of a displayed row. The outputs from the NAND gates are fed as inputs along

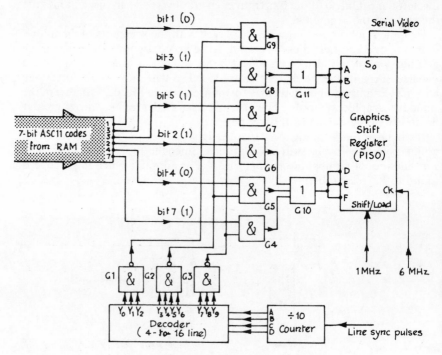

Fig. 6.32 Contiguous graphic generator.

with the appropriate data bits to the AND gates G4–G9. The logic state of the data bits on the diagram is that for the graphics symbol code of Fig. 6.31. Outputs from the AND gates are then combined in the two OR gates G10 and G11.

If the graphics matrix of Fig. 6.30 is considered, it will be seen that the shift register inputs A, B and C correspond to the first 3 'dots' in each matrix row. Since these 3 bits are always at the same state for a given scan line, they may be connected together. During scan lines 1–3, inputs A, B, and C need to be connected to bit 1, for lines 4–7 connected to bit 3 and for scan lines 8–10 connected to bit 5. Similarly, since the shift register inputs D, E, and F correspond to the next 3 'dots' in each matrix row, these inputs may be connected together. During scan lines 1–3, inputs D, E and F need to be connected to bit 2, for lines 4–7 connected to bit 4 and for lines 8–10 connected to bit 7.

Switching of the inputs to the shift register to the appropriate bits and at the correct instants is achieved by the network of AND and OR gates with the gating signals applied from one of the three NAND gates. Table 6.3 shows the logic state of the inputs during the 10 scan lines appropriate to the display of the graphic symbol given in Fig. 6.31. Reading across and down the table it will be seen that the serial dot video produced by the shift register will be in accordance with the 6 segments of the graphics matrix.

Scan line	Output G_1	G_2	G_3	Output G_4	G_5	G_6	G_7	Output G_8	G_9	G_{10}	G_{11}	Shift Register Input A	B	C	D	E	F
0	1	0	0	0	0	1	0	0	0	1	0	0	0	0	1	1	1
1	1	0	0	0	0	1	0	0	0	1	0	0	0	0	1	1	1
2	1	0	0	0	0	1	0	0	0	1	0	0	0	0	1	1	1
3	0	1	0	0	0	0	0	1	0	0	1	1	1	1	0	0	0
4	0	1	0	0	0	0	0	1	0	0	1	1	1	1	0	0	0
5	0	1	0	0	0	0	0	1	0	0	1	1	1	1	0	0	0
6	0	1	0	0	0	0	0	1	0	0	1	1	1	1	0	0	0
7	0	0	1	1	0	0	1	0	0	1	1	1	1	1	1	1	1
8	0	0	1	1	0	0	1	0	0	1	1	1	1	1	1	1	1
9	0	0	1	1	0	0	1	0	0	1	1	1	1	1	1	1	1

Table 6.3 Logic state of bits applied to shift register during 10 scan lines to display graphic symbol of Fig. 6.31

SCREEN CURSOR

When the V.D.U. operator is composing text on the display screen, a **cursor** may be used to indicate the next location in the RAM that a character will be written. Commonly the cursor is a flashing bar or block which moves

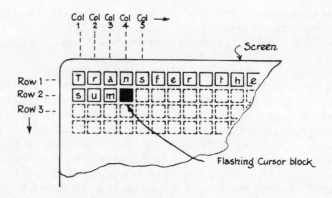

Fig. 6.33 Cursor.

along the character rows as the screen is filled with text, see Fig. 6.33. In the diagram the cursor is pointing to column 4 of row 2 which is the address of the RAM into which the next character will be written when a keystroke is completed by the operator. Thus if key **s** is pressed, this character will be written into column 4, row 2 of the RAM and subsequently when the memory is 'read' the character **s** will appear on the screen. On completion of the keystroke the cursor will point to column 5 of row 2. Operating 'carriage return' sends the cursor to the beginning of the row.

Cursor Generation

A method illustrating the basic idea of cursor generation is given in Fig. 6.34. The RAM has two address generators, 'read' and 'write'. The 'write' address generator has its output incremented by one each time a valid code is produced by the keyboard encoder by means of a strobe pulse fed to it. Thus the 'write' address remains **static** until a key is depressed by the operator, the 'write' address is always one more than the address of the last character to be displayed on the screen or 'read' from the RAM.

The 'read' address generator, however, **continually scans** the RAM locations during the 'read' mode at the normal display timing rate, see Fig. 6.29. This address generator is also responsible for the generation of a read/write control signal. Outputs from the 'write' and 'read' address generators are also fed to a comparator which produces a pulse output when a 'match' occurs between the static address of the write address generator and the scanning address of the read address generator. The pulse only lasts for the period of the 'match', *i.e.* one character period of 1µs, but is repeated on 10 consecutive line scans in each field period.

The 'match' pulse is applied to the AND gate G1 which produces a HIGH at its output of 1µs duration when the cursor control input is at logic 1. This 1µs output pulse is applied via the OR gates G2–G4 to the R, G, and B video

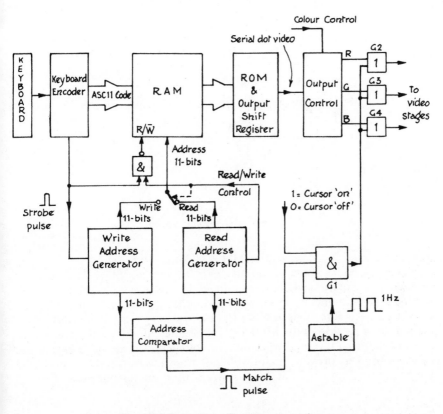

Fig. 6.34 Basic idea of cursor generation.

outputs thus producing on the screen, 1 character space ahead of the last character displayed, a cursor block which is flashed 'on' and 'off' by the astable multivibrator input to G1.

PERIPHERALS

Modem

Data to or from a V.D.U. terminal may be routed over the public telephone network. When this means of data communication is used, it is normal practice to use modulation techniques to convert the binary data logic waveform into voice-frequency signals which the analogue telephone network was designed to handle.

Commonly for bit rates up to 1·2 k-bits/sec, **frequency shift keying** is used, see Fig. 6.35 where the logic 1 and 0 levels of the data logic waveform are converted into audio tones of 1300Hz and 2100Hz respectively. The

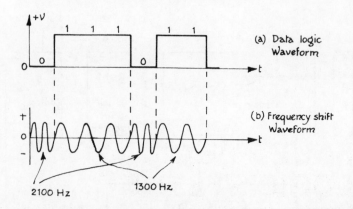

Fig. 6.35 Frequency shift keying.

modulator section of a MODEM (modulator-demodulator) is used to produce the audio tones from the logic waveform, which is a form of frequency modulation where the modulated waveform is always deviated to one of two frequencies. Upon receipt of the signal tones, they must be converted back into logic levels of 1 and 0 and this is carried out in the demodulator section of the MODEM. When the public telephone network is connected to a terminal where mains voltages are present, a **barier unit** must be used to prevent mains voltages from inadvertently entering the telephone line; an isolation transformer is used for this purpose.

Tape Recorder

The data information received by a terminal and stored in its RAM for display is of a volatile nature and will be lost when fresh text is written into the RAM or the terminal is switched 'off'

For some purposes it may be desirable to store particular items of data information as they are received to save time and the cost of accessing the source again, and to recover it at a later time for display. An ordinary audio tape recorder may be used for this purpose, see Fig. 6.1. If the recorder is of the manual only type, it will have to be set to record when a data transmission is expected and stopped when the transmission has ceased. It may then be used to replay the data signal back into the terminal, acting as the data transmission source. Tape recorders with a remote pause control input may be operated automatically by the terminal, using for example, a relay to enable and disable the tape drive motor.

CHAPTER SEVEN

FAULT TRACING ON LOGIC SYSTEMS

FAULT LOCATION IN digital circuits is, in some respects, simpler than with analogue circuits. In a digital system, fault tracing is concerned with the detection of the two logic values of 1 and 0 at voltage levels appropriate to the type of logic family used, *e.g.* TTL, CMOS, ECL *etc*. The logic levels may be static in some parts of the circuit for a period of time, only changing when input conditions alter as with logic gates. In other areas of a system the logic levels may be in the form of repetitive pulses, *e.g.* clock pulses and counter outputs or brief single pulses as with strobe pulses.

In systems where analogue signals are processed, however, it is not only the absence of signal waveforms at various points that cause faults but also changes in waveshape as a result of non-linear operation, parasitic oscillation, spurious noise voltages and intermodulation *etc*; effects which have negligible consequences or are practically rarely found in digital circuits.

Digital circuits do though present special problems, particularly those which are processing non-repetitive signals such as a block of data bytes of different binary coding that are present for only relatively brief periods of time. Also the action of a particular logic gate may rely on the coincidence of short duration input pulses which occur only now and again when a certain action takes place. These special difficulties are compounded in systems using a high clock rate, *e.g.* 10 M-bits/sec and arise due to problems in displaying single short duration pulses or non-repetitive type waveforms; features not catered for with an ordinary c.r.o. which is intended for the display of repetitive type waveforms. There are a number of special fault finding aids and equipment that may by used in digital circuits and these will now be described.

Logic Probes

A logic probe is probably the most useful aid and can be employed for tracing the majority of faults in digital circuits. Its is relatively inexpensive

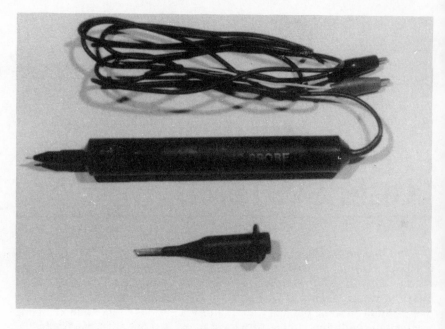

Fig. 7.1 TTL logic probe.

and its compactness makes it an ideal portable servicing tool, see Fig. 7.1. Typically, red and green l.e.ds. are used to indicate the logic 1 and logic 0 levels respectively. The probe may be powered from the logic circuit under test or from an external power source but in this case the negative line must be commoned with the logic systems earth. Some probes are dual purpose, *e.g.* TTL/CMOS but others like the one illustrated are for use with one logic family only. The logic state on a relevant i.c. pin can be detected by applying the probe tip and noting the response of the two l.e.ds.

For TTL, the logic probe has its thresholds set to 0·8V (logic 0) and 2V (logic 1). The static logic circuit states indicated by the probe are shown in Fig. 7.2. When the logic level is at or above the logic 1 threshold of 2V, the

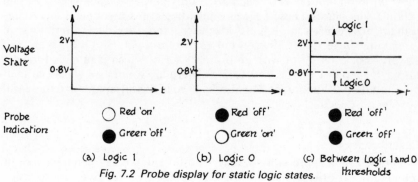

Fig. 7.2 Probe display for static logic states.

red l.e.d. is 'on' and the green l.e.d. is 'off' as in Fig. 7.2(a). If the logic level is at or below the logic 0 thresholds of 0·8V, the red l.e.d. will be 'off' and the green l.e.d. will be 'on' as in Fig. 7.2(b). Should, however, the voltage level in a circuit lie between the logic 1 and 0 thresholds as in Fig. 7.2(c), both l.e.ds. will be 'off'; a display condition which also applies if the point under test is o/c (floating).

Fig. 7.3 shows the type of faults that can occur at gate outputs which may be detected with a logic probe. If the gate output is permanently stuck at

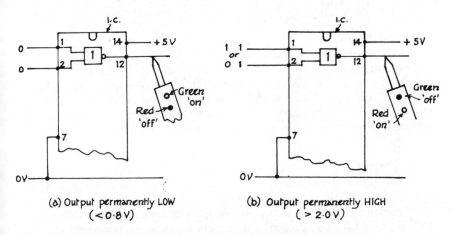

(a) Output permanently LOW   (b) Output permanently HIGH
        (< 0·8 V)   (> 2·0 V)

Fig. 7.3 TTL gate output permanently LOW or HIGH.

logic 0 as in Fig. 7.3(a) irrespective of the logic conditions at the input (which may be tested with the probe), possible faults are:

1) +5V supply line o/c internally or externally.
2) Internal transistor short.

Should the gate output be permanently stuck at logic 1 as in Fig. 7.3(b), possible faults are:

1) OV line o/c internally of externally.
2) Internal transistor short.
3) Internal transistor o/c.

When using the probe to determine the input/output levels of an i.c. always check the levels on the actual i.c. pins rather than on printed circuit lines or board connections to avoid missing o/c lines. Note that the probe may be used to check for the presence of a voltage on the +5V supply line (but not the magnitude) and the 0V level which is useful for quickly eliminating o/c feeds.

Pulse Detection

Logic probes are not restricted to static level testing. Light emitting diodes are high speed devices with light rise and fall times which are usually less than 100ns. However, to be able to visually detect short duration pulses it is necessary to lengthen the pulses. This may be achieved by incorporating into the probe a transient detector and, say, a monostable oscillator. When the narrow pulse is detected the transient may be used to trigger the monostable which provides an output pulse of about 100ms. Thus if a probe is connected to a point which is at logic 0 and experiences a positive going pulse having a duration as little as 30ns, the green l.e.d. is pulsed 'off' for about 100ms which is long enough for an observer to detect. Short duration negative-going pulses may also be detected causing the red l.e.d. to flash 'off' for about 100ms.

The diagrams of Fig. 7.4 shows the expected l.e.d. indications for pulses of various durations and p.r.fs. Thus a logic probe is useful for detecting clock pulses (up to about 20MHz), couter outputs, strobe pulses *etc*. The full versatility of a particular logic probe can only be achieved by carefully studying the manufacturers instruction sheet since manufacturers adopt different specifications for the pulse timings.

Logic Pulsers

A logic pulser is essentially a compact pulse generator and in appearance is similar to a logic probe, see Fig. 7.5

Pulsers normally have a tri-state output which means that they can pulse HIGH and LOW but present a high impedance when not operating. This feature permits the pulser to be left connected without interfering with the logic circuit under test. The pulser is powered from the logic circuit under test via its clip leads and the one illustrated will deliver either a single pulse, a group of 4 pulses or a continuous train of pulses, the operation being selected by a 3-position slide switch. To prevent excessive dissipation in the devices under test, the pulses are of short duration (0·8µs for TTL and 1·8µs for CMOS) at a repetition rate of 1KHz thus maintaining a low mean power dissipation.

To use the pulser, the tip is connected to the logic node or gate input, the appropriate option selected and the push button operated. The pulser then automatically drives the circuits connected to it producing a brief change in logic state which may be detected with a logic probe or c.r.o. The pulses produced are capable of sinking or sourcing up to about 0·5A which ensures sufficient current to overide an i.c. output in either the LOW or HIGH state. The probe has a fan-out of 10, *i.e.* it will drive 10 TTL gates simultaneously.

When considering the operation of the logic probe at gate outputs it was assumed that suitable logic levels were present at the gate inputs. Sometimes a gate input is only present in a logic system, for example, when a transducer is activated and this may occur infrequently. Thus the pulser may be used to replace the transducer source enabling circuit testing to be carried out when ever desired.

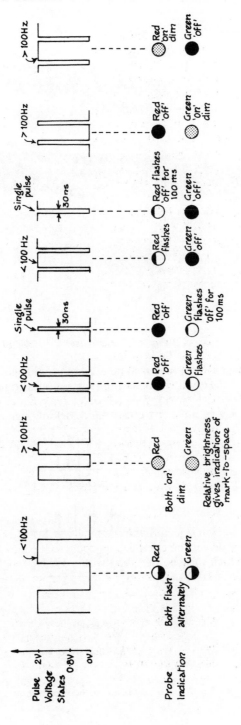

Fig. 7.4 Interpretation of display indication for logic pulses.

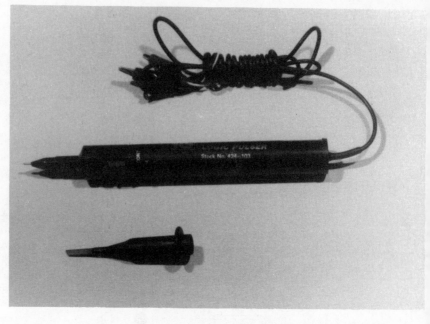

Fig. 7.5 Logic pulser (TTL/CMOS).

The pulser output may also be used to provide clocking of a counter, see Fig. 7.6. Occasionally in a counting system false counts occur which may be due to a defective clocking signal, defective counter or the pick-up of noise impulses. By inhibiting the normal clocking signal and substituting the

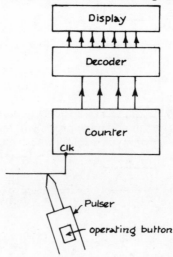

Fig. 7.6 Use of pulser to check operation of counter.

pulser output instead, the operation of the counter may be checked. If the single pulse or 4 pulse output is selected, then at each depression of the pulser button a known number of pulses are applied to the counter to alter the display reading accordingly. This 'slow clocking' of the counter enables faults to be more easily detected.

Additional uses for the pulser output during fault location include trigger pulse for monostable oscillators, clock pulse for flip-flops, strobe pulse for various gate operations and the checking of bus and printed circuit lines.

Current Probe

Consider the diagram of Fig. 7.7. where with the aid of a logic voltage probe the output of G1 has been found to be stuck at logic 0. It may be assumed that G1 is defective and upon replacement this assumption may prove to be correct, however this **is not the only interpretation** of the fault symptom.

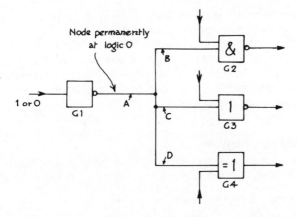

Fig. 7.7 Output of one gate stuck at logic 0 in combinational gate circuit.

The same symptoms will result if there is a short circuit to the 0V line on the printed circuit lines A, B, C or D or a short circuit in either of the gate inputs G2, G3 or G4. Although a voltage probe will indicate that a fault is present at G1 output, it will not reveal exactly where the short circuit exists. What is needed here is a means of finding out where the current is being diverted to without resorting to the breaking of printed circuit tracks or the removal of i.cs. To detect current flow without breaking its path, a detector is required that will sense the **magnetic field** set-up by the current in the conducting path.

Detection of direct currents is difficult (although not impossible) due to the sensitivity required for the levels encountered in digital circuits. Pulsed current detection is easier to achieve and an inductive sensor is one possibility. The idea is illustrated in Fig. 7.8 where the output of G1 has been

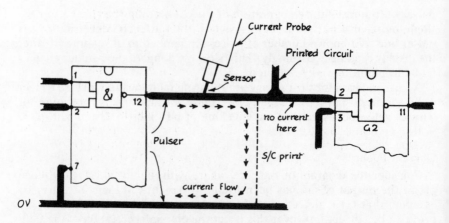

Fig. 7.8 Use of current probe to check for s/c print.

found to be permanently stuck at logic 0. With the supplies to the digital circuit switched 'off', the output of a logic pulser operating in the 'continuous mode' is applied to the circuit as shown. The current probe is then moved along the circuit until no current is registered thus pin-pointing the position of the short circuit. It should be noted that pulsed currents cannot be detected along paths incorporating decoupling capacitors as the capacitors will short out the pulsed currents.

I.C. Clips and Logic Monitors

Other useful aids to fault location include logic clips and logic monitors. An i.c. clip, see Fig. 7.9 will clip quickly and easily on to a standard dual

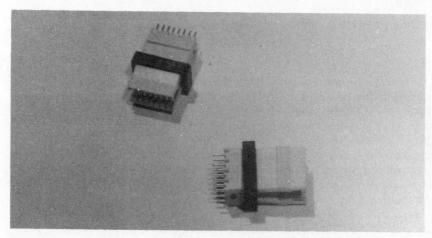

Fig. 7.9 I.C. clips.

in-line i.c. package to bring out the i.c. pins for testing. A logic probe may then be attached to the extended pins for testing thus reducing the risk of accidental shorting out of pins. Test clips with 16, 28 or 40 pins are usually available.

A logic monitor or checker is a device, see Fig. 7.10 which clips onto the i.c. under test to instantly indicate the logic state of each pin. It derives its power from the i.c. supply regardless of which pins the supply is applied to. This is achieved by internal monitoring circuits which sense the highest voltage present (the d.c. supply voltage) and use this to provide for the display devices and circuitry of the monitor. The logic state of each pin is indicated by light emitting diodes, usually red. When an indicator is extinguished it represents logic 0 (LOW) and when illuminated logic 1 (HIGH) or open circuit.

Fig. 7.10 Logic monitor.

The logic monitor is most useful for analysing the static logic state of a circuit or the low frequency dynamic state. High frequency logic systems may be checked by slowing down the clock rate, *i.e.* disconnecting the internal clock and substituting the output of a logic pulser where this is possible. Logic monitors are usually available to clip on to 14 or 16 pin dual in-line i.cs.

Logic Analyser

A logic analyser is an instrument that is designed to record the logic levels at a number of points or channels simultaneously. It is capable of providing more detailed and searching tests on digital and microprocessor circuits in particular than the test devices previously considered. Logic analysers are typically provided with 8, 16 or 32 input channels which can be used to study the behaviour of logic signals on the data, address or control bus of a digital system or its input/output ports. The signals applied to the input channels are not recorded continuously as with an ordinary c.r.o. but are sampled at specified instants and then stored in the analyser's memory. Once in the analyser's memory the data may be read and analysed at leisure.

Trigger Event

To enable the user to monitor particular areas of a data sequence, all analysers provide a trigger or 'event' selection feature which defines the instant about which data is to be captured by the analyser's memory. The 'trigger event' is a previously defined word or pattern of bits which is selected by the user prior to initiating the recording process.

The recording process commences when the analyser is ARMED at which instant the data applied to the input channels is continuously recorded or written into the analyser's RAM memory. During this period the data applied to the analyser is continuously compared with the 'event' data word and when a 'match' occurs the recording process continues for a further 63 words. As the analyser's memory is typically 128 words long, the final data captured by the memory consists of 64 words prior to the trigger event and 63 words after the trigger event, see Fig. 7.11. Capturing data prior to the

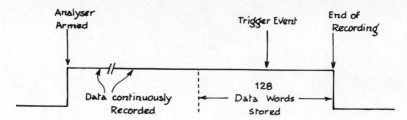

Fig. 7.11 Data recording sequence.

trigger event is a form of negative time recording and may be explained by reference to Fig. 7.12 which illustrates the storage of data in the analyser's memory.

Once the analyser has been ARMED, data is continuously recorded and data will be written into the memory commencing at row 1. Assuming that the data prior to the selected trigger event lasts for more than 128 clock cycles, *i.e.* is greater than 128 bytes in length, then when row 128 has been filled with data the following data bytes will over-write the data held in rows 1, 2, 3 *etc.* When the trigger event is detected, the 'write' operation continues for a further 63 bytes thus the memory will always hold 64 bytes of data prior to the trigger event and 63 bytes after the trigger event. Of course, the trigger event may not necessarily occur on row 65 as depicted but on any row; the format of the captured data will however be precisely the same. Most analysers permit extra conditions to be placed on the trigger event. This

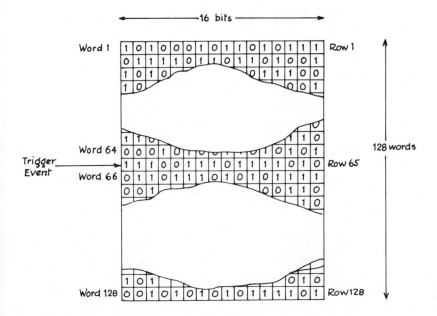

Fig. 7.12 Capturing data prior to and after trigger event in analyser's memory.

'trigger qualifier' feature allows the user to set the trigger event to occur, say, after **n** repetitions of the trigger word or **n** clock cycles after the trigger word.

Clock and Clock Qualifier

An analyser requires a clock signal to strobe the channel data words into its memory. The clocking signal may be derived from the clock of the digital system under test or from the analyser's own internal clock. When using an external clock, the user is able to select whether leading or trailing edge triggering of the clock is to be employed. The diagram of Fig. 7.13 illustrates trailing-edge triggering of the clock and the resultant stored data words from the input channels (8 channels assumed).

Since data is only transferred to the analyser's memory on the clock edges, any changes in the data waveform such as that produced by the interfering spike or 'glitch' of channel 1 input will go unnoticed. The maximum time that a data signal change can go unnoticed is the periodic time of the clock signal, known as the 'sampling ambiguity'. To reduce the ambiguity, analysers employing their own internal clock use clock oscillators operating at frequencies several times the data rate of the digital system under test.

In some digital circuit applications it may not be necessary to store data on all clock edges. Thus an extra input know as a 'clock qualifier' may be provided to select particular clock edges when data is present, see Fig. 7.14. The clock and clock qualifier inputs are ANDed togther so that a qualified clock signal is produced only when the clock qualifier is in the logic 1 state.

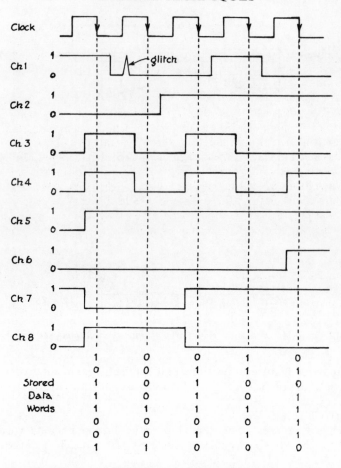

Fig. 7.13 Use of external clock to strobe data into analyser's memory.

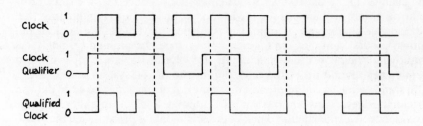

Fig. 7.14 Qualified clock generation.

This permits, for example, the read/write address control line of a digital system memory to act as a clock qualifier so that the analyser monitors the data on the bus of a system memory during, say, the read operaion only.

Display Modes

Logic analysers usually permit two main types of display. One display mode provides a data listing, see Fig. 7.15(a) where each data word from the stored 8, 16 or 32 channel inputs is sampled on a clock edge. Each data word is then displayed in a suitable code, *e.g.* binary, hexadecimal or ASCII. If the data word is given in binary, the data listing will show the logic 1 and 0 levels on the input channels. The other form of display is the timing display where the logic waveforms of the various data channels are displayed one under the other to show their relative timing, see Fig. 7.15(b). A flashing cursor may be provided that may be moved to enable the identification of each data word from the waveform display. It should be realised that any glitches present in

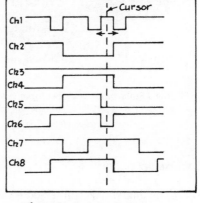

Clock No.	Data
00	002A
01	0028
02	1A3B
03	00FF
04	0FA8
05	FFFE
06	0C10
07	03A4
08	3FFF
09	4A2F
0A	13AE
0B	0005

(a) Data Listing in Hexadecimal   (b) Data Timing Display

Fig. 7.15 Two common display modes.

the input data channel waveforms will only show up in the timing display if they were present at the clocking instant when data was transferred to the analyser's memory. Internal clocking, at a rate higher than the system clock rate is more likely to reveal such disturbances, but a larger memory capacity will be required to reduce the period that signal changes go unnoticed whilst maintaining the same data byte storage capability.

The illustration of Fig. 7.16 shows a logic analyser in the timing mode with an 8-trace display provided by an ordinary c.r.o. under the control of the analyser. In more sophisticated analysers, the display is built into the analyser.

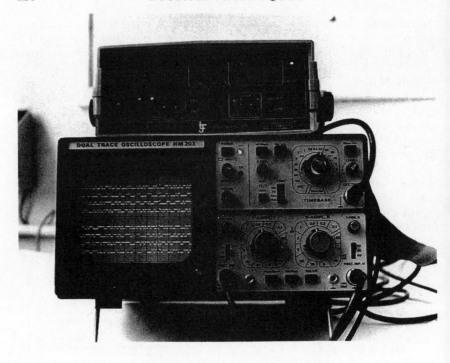

Fig. 7.16 LJ Electronics Ltd, SA1 logic analyser used with ordinary c.r.o. to produce an 8-trace or 16-trace display.

Application Examples

One example showing the use of a logic analyser is illustrated in Fig. 7.17 where the analyser is connected to check the operation of an 8-bit counter. The trigger event may be set so that storage of the input data commences at, say, 00000000 or at any count that is desirable. When in the display timing mode, the waveform output from each stage of the counter will be displayed one under the other showing the relative timing of the waveforms. Any malfunction of the counter such as a short in the i.c. between Q_c and Q_d outputs or intermittent operation will readily show up in the displayed waveforms. The trigger qualifier may be used to check the counter operation after a number of trigger events for the detection of obscure faults that only reveal themselves after a number of count cycles have been completed.

Another example is illustrated in Fig. 7.18 where an analyser is used to check the contents of a ROM. Here, it may be preferred to utilise the data listing mode of operaion so that the stored data byte at each memory location may be read-off quickly from the display. This arrangement may be used to isolate faults in a logic system where instructions or operations fail to give the correct results and where it is desirable to check the source of such

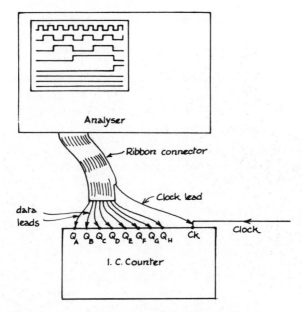

Fig. 7.17 Checking a counter with a logic analyser.

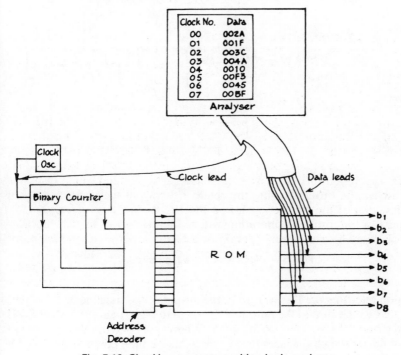

Fig. 7.18 Checking a memory with a logic analyser.

instructions when they originate from a memory, whether it be a ROM, RAM or EPROM *etc*. The trigger event may be set to occur at any known data word stored in the ROM so that particular instructions or data may be verified.

An analyser may also be used to check the operation of a scanning keyboard encoder to verify that the correct code is generated for each of the depressed keys.

Logic Systems

A logic system illustrating the operation of a digital voltmeter (d.v.m.) using a dual-slope integrator is given in Fig, 7.19 The voltmeter is reset by operating the 'Reset Button' which applies a short duration pulse from the single-shot clock to the reset input of the counter via the inverter gate G2. This action clears the contents of the counter and sets the Q output of the Latch to logic 1.

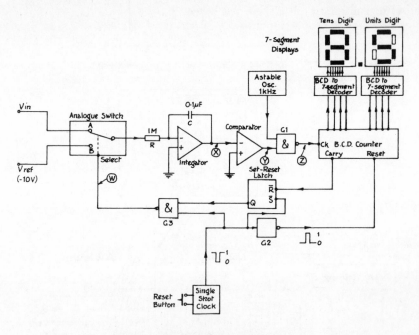

Fig. 7.19 Digital voltmeter logic system.

Upon releasing the Reset Button, the output of the single-shot clock goes to logic 1 which caused the output of G3 to go to logic 0 since the other input of G3 (from the Latch) is also at logic 1. When applied to the 'select' input of the analogue switch it causes the switch to take-up the position shown (A), connecting the voltage to be measured (V_{in}) to the input of the Integrator.

With V_{in} between 0V and +10V, the integrator output will ramp down from 0V at V_{in}/CR volts/sec, see waveforms of Fig. 7.20. Whilst the integrator output is below 0V, the comparator output will be HIGH at logic 1 allowing 1kHz pulses from the astable to be gated into the clock input of the B.C.D counter. The counter will then count-up. After a period equal to 100ms (100 clock pulses) the 2-decade counter will have reached a count of 100 which will cause the 'carry-out' of the counter to go LOW (logic 0). As a result the Q output of the Latch will be reset to logic 0 and the output of G3 will go to logic 0. This action will place the analogue switch in position B connecting the reference voltage (V_{ref}) of −10V to the input of the integrator.

With this negative input voltage, the integrator output will ramp-up with a slope of V_{ref}/CR volts/sec. Whilst the integrator output ramps-up towards 0V, clock pulses will continue to increment the counter (note that when the counter previously reached a count of 100 it would have reset). As soon as the integrator output exceeds 0V, the comparator output will go LOW thereby inhibiting any further clock pulses to the counter. The counter output registered on the display will be a number between 00 and 99, the value of which is proportional to the analogue input voltage V_{in}.

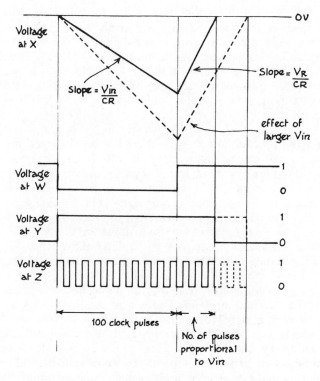

Fig. 7.20 Waveforms explaining operation of DVM.

The use of a dual-slope integrator provides good accuracy for the voltmeter which is only dependant upon the stability of the reference voltage. The system shown has a resolution of 0·1V, *i.e.* each pulse counted represents 0·1V. By increasing the number of counting decades, the resolution may be improved. This will, however, increase the conversion time which may be off-set by increasing the clock frequency.

Logic system diagrams and explanation of operation for a frequency meter and timer are given in Chapter 2 and for a character generator in Chapter 6.

CLOCK OSCILLATORS

Most digital systems require a clock pulse generator or oscillator that will deliver a train of rectangular pulses so that synchronisation of the various logic operations within the system may be achieved. The important features of a clock generator are good frequency stablity, low output impedance to give easy drive capability, clean output waveform shape and defined logic levels to suit the logic family used within the system.

Crystal Controlled Clock Oscillators

Digital systems operating at high frequencies *e.g.* 1MHz and above normally use a clock oscillator with crystal control on account of its high degree of stability in operating frequency, see Fig. 7.21(a). The sinusoidal signal generated by the crystal oscillator is usually fed out via a buffer amplifier which reduces the loading effect of following stages hence increasing the frequency and amplitude stability and also provides a low impedance output.

To produce a rectangular clocking waveform, the output from the buffer stage is applied to a Schmitt Trigger operating as a 'squarer' providing an output waveform having sharp rise and fall times. In many systems, sub-multiples of the clock signal frequency are required for timing purposes, *e.g.* the clock may operate at the data bit rate but a byte rate clocking signal is often required. The sub-multiple timing signals may be obtained by passing the clock signal into a frequency divider stage(s) and binary or divide-by-n counters may be used for this purpose as illustrated.

With data transmission systems particularly those operating at high frequencies, not only should the clock have the correct frequency but also have the correct phase relationship with the received data. In these circumstances, an automatic phase lock loop may be employed so that the data clock acquires frequency and phase synchronisation with the received data. The 'reference' signal for such a system may be the received data itself, a synchronising signal at the data bit rate or some stable signal at a sub-multiple of the data bit rate.

The arrangement of Fig. 7.21(b) illustrates how a sub-multiple of the desired clock signal rate may be used as the 'reference' input. The crystal clock oscillator operating at 16MHz provides the system clock signal at

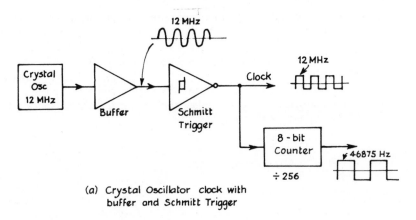

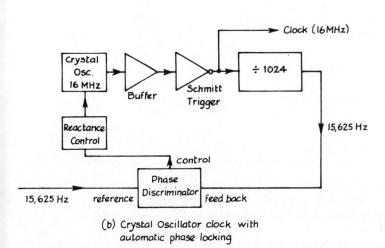

(a) Crystal Oscillator clock with buffer and Schmitt Trigger

(b) Crystal Oscillator clock with automatic phase locking

Fig. 7.21

16MHz but this is divided-down and supplied as the 'feedback' input to the phase discriminator along with the 'reference' input which is assumed to be 15625Hz. If a frequency or phase error exists between the 'reference' and 'feedback' due to, say, thermal effects on the crystal oscillator, the phase discriminator gives out an 'error' voltage which via the reactance stage (incorporating, say, a varactor diode) corrects the frequency or phase of the oscillator.

Non-Crystal Controlled Clock Oscillators

In some digital systems, often low frequency ones, the specification placed on the frequency tolerance of the systems clock is not too close and there are a number of pulse type oscillators that may be usefully employed. A Schmitt trigger can be arranged as an astable multivibrator, the principle of which was described in Chapter 2 (Fig. 2.85). A practical circuit suitable for use in the frequency range of 100Hz to 1MHz is given in Fig. 7.22 together with associated waveforms and component values. The capacitor C alternately charges and discharges between the upper and lower threshold limits as shown causing the Schmitt trigger to rapidly switch when these limits are reached. When using a 5V supply a pulse train having a mark-to-space ratio of 1:3 will be obtained at the output.

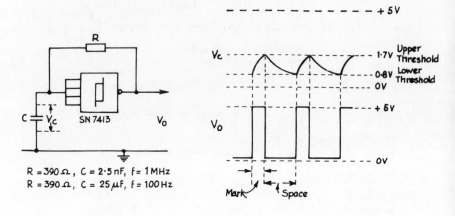

R = 390 Ω, C = 2·5 nF, f = 1MHz
R = 390 Ω, C = 25 μF, f = 100 Hz

Fig. 7.22

Another technique that may be used to produce a clock oscillator is by the interconnection of a number of basic **logic gates**. A logic gate astable multivibrator is given in Fig. 7.23(a). NAND or NOR gates may be used since they are connected as inverters and both gates include amplification. The arrangement shown is for TTL but if CMOS devices are used another resistor is placed in series with the input to G1 to protect the input diodes of the gate.

The positive feedback from the output of G2 to the input of G1 via C1 causes the astable to rapidly change states. Assume that the output of G2 has just gone HIGH (+3·6V). The input to G2 must therefore be LOW at approximately 0V as will be the output of G1. The input to G1 must be at the **threshold voltage** (+2V). When G2 output goes HIGH the rise of almost 3·6V is passsed via C1 to the input of G1 taking G1 input voltage to +5·6V. These voltage states are shown in Fig.7.23 (b). Thus C1 is connected on one side to +3·6V and on the other side to 0V via R1. Accordingly C1 charges at a rate determined by the time constant C1, R1 seconds.

As C1 charges, G1 input voltage falls and when it has fallen to the threshold value of +2V the output of G1 switches to the HIGH state of +3·6V. As a result the output of G2 goes LOW. The fall in voltage at G2 output is passed via C1 to the input of G1 causing G1 input voltage to fall to

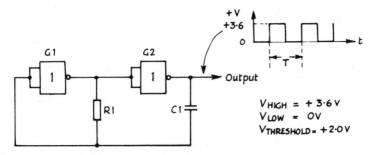

(a) Basic arrangement with NOR gates connected as inverters

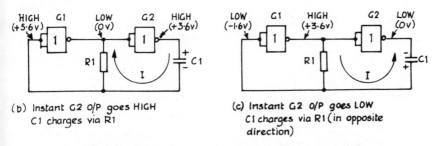

(b) Instant G2 O/P goes HIGH
C1 charges via R1

(c) Instant G2 O/P goes LOW
C1 charges via R1 (in opposite
direction)

Fig. 7.23

$-1\cdot6$V. These voltage states are shown in the diagram of Fig. 7.23(c) causing C1 to charge in the oposite direction on a time constant C1, R1 seconds. As C1 charges the input voltage to G1 rises and just before it reaches $+2$V the circuit changes state once more and so on. Thus at G2 output a rectangular wave is obtained as (shown opposite phase at G1 output). The periodic time T is given by approximately:

$$T = 2\cdot2 \; C1 \; R1 \; secs.$$

If R1 = $5\cdot6$k-ohm and C1 = $4\cdot7$nF,

$$f = \frac{1}{T} = \frac{1}{2\cdot2 \times 5\cdot6 \times 10^3 \times 4\cdot7 \times 10^{-9}} = 17270 Hz$$

Another type of logic gate oscillator is shown in the diagrams of Fig. 7.24. This uses 3 inverter gates forming a **ring oscillator** utilising negative feedback, see Fig. 7.24(a). The eqivalent circuit for a single inverter stage is shown in Fig. 7.24(b) where the propagation delay (switching time) may be represented by a CR network and the inverter gate is ideal (switches instantaneously). Thus any change in voltage state at the output of 1 inverter gate cannot be communicated to the following gate until C has charged (or discharged) via R.

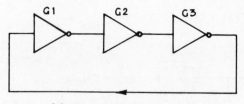

(a) Ring oscillator using 3 invertors

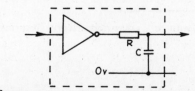

(b) Equivalent Circuit of single stage where
the time constant CR = propagation delay

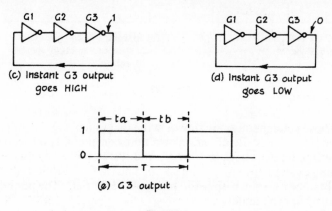

(c) Instant G3 output   (d) Instant G3 output
     goes HIGH   goes LOW

(e) G3 output

Fig. 7.24

Suppose that the output of G3 has just gone HIGH, see Fig. 7.24(c). Thus G1 input will be HIGH and after a period equal to the propagation delay the input to G2 will go LOW. Following a second propagation delay period the input to G3 will go HIGH and after a third propagation period the output of G3 will go LOW. Thus G3 output will remain HIGH for 3 propagation delay periods. (t_a), see Fig. 7.24(e). The LOW at G3 output, see Fig. 7.24(d) is now fed back to G1 and the changes of state propagate along to G3 output in a similar way so that G3 output remains in the LOW state for 3 propagation delay periods (t_b). The periodic time (T) of the oscillation is given by:

$$T = t_a + t_b = 6 \times \text{propagation delay}.$$

Thus if the propagation delay of each stage is 10 ns,

$$T = 6 \times 10 \text{ ns} = 60 \text{ ns}$$

$$\text{thus } f = \frac{1}{60 \times 10^{-9}} \text{ Hz}$$

$$= 16 \cdot 67 \text{MHz}$$

The frequency of oscillation may be reduced by using 5 inverter gates with the output of the fifth gate connected to the input of the first resulting in a periodic time of 10 × propagation delay. Alternatively, since the frequency of oscillation will still be quite high (10MHz), the frequency may be reduced by connecting a CR network as shown in Fig. 7.25. Using TTL NAND gates operating from a 5V supply and with C = 1270pF and R = 4·7k-ohm, a rectangular pulse output having a mark-to-space ratio of 5:1 may be obtained at a frequency of 85kHz. Other types of clock oscillators include operational amplifiers such as the 555 connected as an astable multivibrator, unijunction relaxation oscillators and specialised integrated circuits such as the 4047B (astable oscillator).

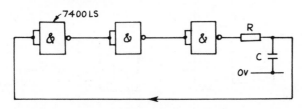

Fig. 7.25

The output of any clock oscillator must be able to drive the required number of logic gates of counters *etc* without degrading the clock waveshape, *i.e.* without lengthening the rise and fall times or introducing ringing. When the clock path intoduces a relatively high capacitive load to the clock oscillator, the clock output must have a low impedance so that the capacitive load can be rapidly charged and discharged. Thus a special buffer or interface circuit may be required between the clock oscillator and the circuits it supplies.

LOGIC CIRCUIT SYMBOLS

Gate	British Standard	U.S. Mil. Standard

BASIC LOGIC GATES

Logic Function

Truth Table

AND
(2 or more inputs)

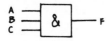

The output assumes the 1 state
only if all the inputs assume
the 1 state.

Inputs			Output
A	B	C	F
0	0	0	0
0	0	1	0
0	1	0	0
0	1	1	0
1	0	0	0
1	0	1	0
1	1	0	0
1	1	1	1

OR
(2 or more inputs)

The output assumes the 1 state
if one or more inputs assume
the 1 state.

A	B	C	F
0	0	0	0
0	0	1	1
0	1	0	1
0	1	1	1
1	0	0	1
1	0	1	1
1	1	0	1
1	1	1	1

NOT
(Single input)

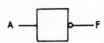

The output assumes the 1 state
only if the input is not at the
1 state (inverter).

A	F
0	1
1	0

Logic Function   Truth Table

NAND
(2 or more inputs)

This is the AND function followed
by the NOT function, *i.e.* the
truth table is the opposite to
that for the AND function.

Inputs			Output
A	B	C	F
0	0	0	1
0	0	1	1
0	1	0	1
0	1	1	1
1	0	0	1
1	0	1	1
1	1	0	1
1	1	1	0

NOR
(2 or more inputs)

This is the OR function followed
by the NOT function and the truth
table is opposite to the OR function.

A	B	C	F
0	0	0	1
0	0	1	0
0	1	0	0
0	1	1	0
1	0	0	0
1	0	1	0
1	1	0	0
1	1	1	0

EX–OR
(usually 2 inputs)

The output assumes the 1 state if one
and only one input assumes the 1 state,
i.e. if the inputs are of different state.

A	B	F
0	0	0
0	1	1
1	0	1
1	1	0

EX–NOR
(usually 2 inputs)

The output assumes the 1 state only if
all the inputs are of the same logic state,
i.e. the inputs are coincident.

A	B	F
0	0	1
0	1	0
1	0	0
1	1	1

BOOLEAN EXPRESSIONS

'BOOLEAN' OR 'SWITCHING' Algebra is a convenient way of representing the action of logic gates or systems and is simpler than truth tables, particularly when there is a large number of inputs. The symbols used relate to the fundamental logic gate operations of AND, OR and NOT:

Logic Function   Boolean Expression

        AND $F = A \cdot B$ (where . means AND)
F (the output) is at logic 1 if the inputs A and B are both at logic 1.

        OR $F = A + B$ (where + means OR)
F is at logic 1 if A or B is at logic 1.

        NOT $F = \bar{A}$ (where $\bar{A}$ means the opposite of A)
F is at logic 1 when A is not at logic 1.

Thus for NAND and NOR we have:

        NAND $F = \overline{A \cdot B}$

        NOR $F = \overline{A + B}$

and for EX–OR and EX–NOR we have:

        EX–OR $F = (A \cdot \bar{B}) + (\bar{A} \cdot B)$

        EX–NOR $F = (A \cdot B) + (\bar{A} \cdot \bar{B})$

To be able to reduce complex Boolean expressions to a simpler form, the following theorems are useful, some of which can be illustrated with the aid of simple switch circuits.

(1) $A + 0 = A$

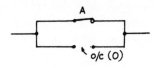

(2) A + 1 = 1

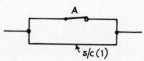

(3) A + A = A

(4) A + Ā = 1

(5) A . 0 = 0

(6) A . 1 = A

(7) A . A = A

(8) A . Ā = 0

(9) Ā̄ = A   no suitable switch analogy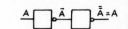

(10) A + B = B + A

(11) B (A + Ā) = B

(12) A + (A . B) = A

(13) $A (A + B) = A$

(14) $A + (\bar{A} . B) = A + B$

(15) $A (\bar{A} + B) = A . B$

(16) $A . B . C = A (B . C) = C (A . B)$
Grouping of switches has no effect

(17) $A + B + C = A + (B + C) = C + (A + B)$
Grouping of switches has no effect

(18) $A (B + C) = (A . B) + (A . C)$

(19) $A + (B . C) = (A + B) . (A + C)$

De Morgans Theorem

De Morgans theorem states that for 2 variables:

$$\overline{A \cdot B} = \bar{A} + \bar{B}$$

and

$$\overline{A + B} = \bar{A} \cdot \bar{B}$$

or for 3 variables

$$\overline{A \cdot B \cdot C} = \bar{A} + \bar{B} + \bar{C}$$

and

$$\overline{A + B + C} = \bar{A} \cdot \bar{B} \cdot \bar{C}$$

The rule here is to 'split' the negation symbol over the variables and change the sign. De Morgans theorem which is a valuable aid to simplification of Boolean expressions, may be verified by truth tables.

Forming the Boolean expression from a logic circuit

Consider the logic circuit shown under. The Boolean expression for the output F may be developed by forming the Boolean expression for each gate in turn commencing at the input(s) as shown.

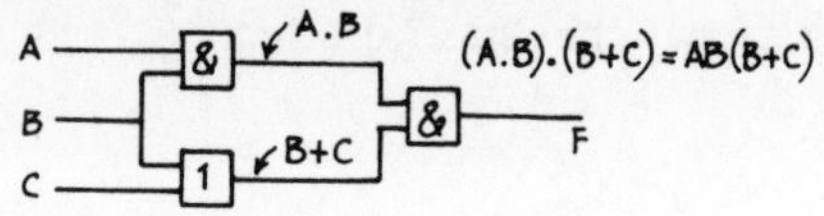

The final expression may be simplified as follows:

$$F = A.B (B + C)$$

multiplying out we have

$$
\begin{aligned}
F &= (A.B.B) + (A.B.C) \\
&= (A.B) + (A.B.C) \quad B.B = B \ (7) \\
&= A.B (1 + C) \quad \text{Dividing each term by A.B} \\
&= A.B \quad 1 + C = 1 \ (2)
\end{aligned}
$$

Thus input C is redundant and the above logic circuit may be replaced by:

Forming the Boolean Expression From a Truth Table

Consider the truth table below:

Condition	Inputs			Output
	A	B	C	F
1	0	0	0	0
2	0	0	1	0
3	0	1	0	0
4	0	1	1	1
5	1	0	0	0
6	1	0	1	0
7	1	1	0	1
8	1	1	1	1

To form a Boolean expression using the truth table, the first step is to note the condition(s) in the table that result in logic 1 at the output. It will be seen that in this case a logic 1 is obtained for condition 4 **or** condition 7 **or** condition 8. The next step is to note the logic conditions of the inputs that result in a logic 1 at the output and for each combination to form a Boolean statement thus:

$$\text{Condition } 4 = \bar{A} . B . C$$
$$\text{Condition } 7 = A . B . \bar{C}$$
$$\text{Condition } 8 = A . B . C$$

Finally each statement is ORed with the others thus:

$$F = (\bar{A}.B.C.) + (A.B.\bar{C}) + (A.B.C.)$$

The expression may be simplified as follows:

$$F = B (\bar{A}.C + A.\bar{C} + A.C)$$
$$\text{or} \quad F = B [\bar{A}.C + A(\bar{C} + C)]$$
$$F = B (\bar{A}.C + A) \quad ....(4)$$
$$F = B (A + C) \quad ....(14)$$

The logic diagram is thus:

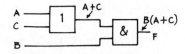

KARNAUGH MAPPING

THE SIMPLIFICATION OF logic expressions using Boolean algebra requires a good knowledge of Boolean laws and identities and often a certain amount of trial and error in placing expressions in the correct form. Karnaugh mapping is a graphical method of simplifying **sum-of-products** Boolean expressions where the expression is displayed on a map of squares.

2-Variable Karnaugh Map

A simple 2-variable Karnaugh map is shown in Fig. A4.1 where A and B are the variables. Since two variables have four possible combinations, the map is divided into four squares or **cells**. One of the variables (A) is placed over the columns of the map where A represents logic 1 and $\bar{A}$ represents logic 0 and the other variable (B) is placed over the rows of the map where B represents logic 1 and $\bar{B}$ represents logic 0.

Each of the squares within the map can, therefore, be used to represent a Boolean expression containing the two variables; square 1 represents the expression $\bar{A}.\bar{B}$, square 2 the expression $A.\bar{B}$, square 3 the expression $\bar{A}.B$ and square 4 the expression $A.B$.

Consider the Boolean expression $F = \bar{A}.B + A.B$. The expression may be **mapped** by placing a 1 in each of the squares which represents a term within the expression, as in Fig. A4.2(a).

The expression may be simplified by grouping (in pairs) squares which

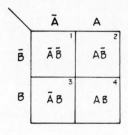

Fig. A4.1 2-variable Karnaugh map.

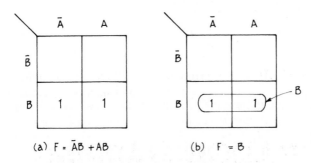

Fig. A4.2 Simplifying a 2-variable expression.

contain a 1 as in Fig. A4.2(b). In this case the encircled group fills half of the map and the common term of the squares in the encircled group is B.

$$\text{Thus } F = B$$

This may be verified by using Boolean algebra:

$$F = \bar{A}.B + A.B$$
$$= B(\bar{A} + A)$$
$$= B \text{ (since } \bar{A} + A = 1)$$

Example 1
Using a Karnaugh map, simplify:

$$F = A.\bar{B} + \bar{A}.B + \bar{A}.\bar{B}$$

Plotting the 1s for the terms in the equation we have the Karnaugh map of Fig. A4.3. Here there are two encircled groups, one group with a common term $\bar{A}$ and the other with a common term $\bar{B}$. The minimised solution is obtained by ORing the groups.

$$\text{Thus } F = \bar{A} + \bar{B}$$

This example shows that adjacent squares containing 1s can be grouped vertically and horizontally (never diagonally) and that groups can overlap containing cells in more than one group.

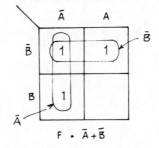

F . $\bar{A} + \bar{B}$

Fig. A4.3 Mapping and simplification of $F = A\bar{B} + \bar{A}B + \bar{A}\bar{B}$.

Example 2

Using a Karnaugh map simplify:

$$F = A.B + \bar{A}.B + A.\bar{B} + \bar{A}.\bar{B}$$

Plotting the 1s for the four terms we have the Karnaugh map of Fig. A4.4. Here there is an encircled group of four 1s which occupies the whole map. This means that the logic function of the terms are redundant since all combinations of A and B are present in the equation and $F = 1$.

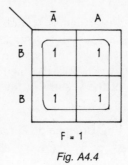

F = 1

Fig. A4.4

3-Variable Karnaugh Map

A Karnaugh map for 3 variables A, B and C is shown in Fig. A4.5. Here two of the variables are grouped together over the columns with the third variable placed along side the rows. Cell 1 now represents the expression $\bar{A}.\bar{B}.\bar{C}$, cell 2 the expression $\bar{A}.B.\bar{C}$, cell 3 the expression $A.B.\bar{C}$ *etc*. Note particularly the manner in which the 2 variables A and B have been labelled; in proceeding from one square to the next across a row or from the last to first square in a row, only one variable changes at a time. Thus square 4 can be considered next to square 1 and square 8 next to square 5.

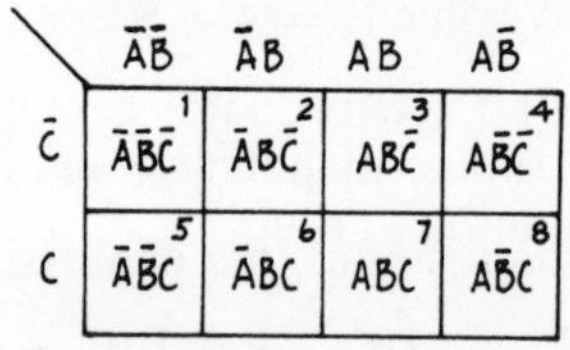

	$\bar{A}\bar{B}$	$\bar{A}B$	AB	$A\bar{B}$
$\bar{C}$	$\bar{A}\bar{B}\bar{C}$ ¹	$\bar{A}B\bar{C}$ ²	$AB\bar{C}$ ³	$A\bar{B}\bar{C}$ ⁴
C	$\bar{A}\bar{B}C$ ⁵	$\bar{A}BC$ ⁶	ABC ⁷	$A\bar{B}C$ ⁸

Fig. A4.5 3-variable Karnaugh map.

Example 3

Using a Karnaugh map, simplify:

$$Z = \bar{A}.\bar{B}.\bar{C}. + \bar{A}.B.\bar{C}. + \bar{A}.B.C. + \bar{A}.\bar{B}.C. + A.\bar{B}.\bar{C}.$$

For each term in the expression, a 1 is plotted on the map as in Fig. A4.6. The largest group is four 1s and these are encircled. A group of two 1s is also present comprising the 1s in the first and last squares of the upper row. The

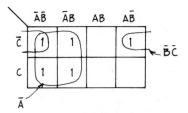

Fig. A4.6

variable common to the group of four is $\bar{A}$ and to the group of two, the variables $\bar{B}.\bar{C}$. Thus the minimised solution is:

$$Z = \bar{A} + \bar{B}.\bar{C}.$$

Example 4

Minimise using a Karnaugh map, the expression:

$$X = \bar{R}.\bar{S}.\bar{T}. + \bar{R}.\bar{S}.T. + S.T. + R.\bar{S}.\bar{T}. + R.\bar{S}.T.$$

Plotting the 1s for each term we have the Karnaugh map of Fig. A4.7. Note that the term S.T is represented by the lower middle two squares. We now have two groups of four. The common term of the group in the lower row is T and the common term of the group at the two sides, which can be considered as adjacent, is $\bar{S}$. Thus the solution is:

$$X = T + \bar{S}.$$

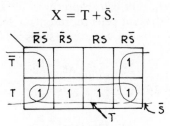

Fig. A4.7

Example 5

Simplify by using a Karnaugh map, the expression:

$$F = \bar{A}.\bar{B}.\bar{C}. + \bar{A}.B.C. + A.B.C. + A.\bar{B}.C.$$

The 1s are plotted on the map as in Fig. A4.8. It will be seen that there are

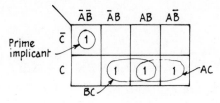

Fig. A4.8

two groups of two 1s also a single 1 which cannot be combined with any other term. Such a term is called a **prime implicant** of the function and must be included in the final minimised expression. The solution is thus:

$$F = \bar{A}.\bar{B}.\bar{C}. + B.C. + A.C.$$

Rules for 3-Variable Karnaugh Maps

1 Note all prime implicants and encircle the corresponding squares.
2 If there are groups of four adjacent terms present, encircle these. This will eliminate two of the variables, leaving in the case of a 3-variable map just a single variable.
3 Encircle any remaining adjacent pairs of terms present. It is not necessary to combine a term in another way if it is already combined.
4 Write down the simplified form of the encircled groups including any prime implicants.

4-Variable Karnaugh Map

Four variables have $2^4 = 16$ possible combinations, thus the map is divided into 16 squares as shown in Fig. A4.9. It should be noted that:

(a) A single cell represents a 4-variable term.
(b) A group of two adjacent cells represents a 3-variable term.
(c) A group of four adjacent cells represents a 2-variable term.
(d) A group of eight adjacent cells represents a 1-variable term.

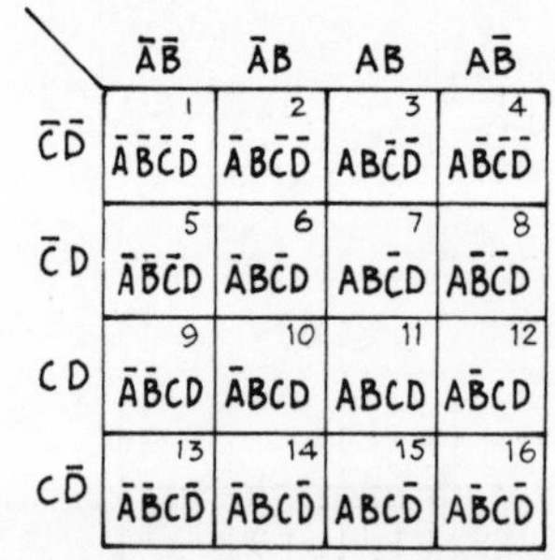

	$\bar{A}\bar{B}$	$\bar{A}B$	AB	$A\bar{B}$
$\bar{C}\bar{D}$	1 $\bar{A}\bar{B}\bar{C}\bar{D}$	2 $\bar{A}B\bar{C}\bar{D}$	3 $AB\bar{C}\bar{D}$	4 $A\bar{B}\bar{C}\bar{D}$
$\bar{C}D$	5 $\bar{A}\bar{B}\bar{C}D$	6 $\bar{A}B\bar{C}D$	7 $AB\bar{C}D$	8 $A\bar{B}\bar{C}D$
CD	9 $\bar{A}\bar{B}CD$	10 $\bar{A}BCD$	11 $ABCD$	12 $A\bar{B}CD$
$C\bar{D}$	13 $\bar{A}\bar{B}C\bar{D}$	14 $\bar{A}BC\bar{D}$	15 $ABC\bar{D}$	16 $A\bar{B}C\bar{D}$

Fig. A4.9 4-variable Karnaugh map.

Example 6
Simplify:

$$F = A.B.\bar{C}.\bar{D} + \bar{A}.B.\bar{C}.D + A.B.\bar{C}.D + \bar{A}.\bar{B}.C.D + A.\bar{B}.C.D + A.B.C.\bar{D}$$

The simplified solution, see Fig. A4.10, is:

$$F = B.\bar{C}.D + A.B.\bar{D} + \bar{B}.C.D$$

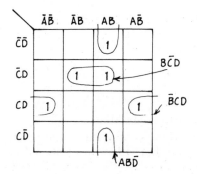

Fig. A4.10

Note that squares in the top and bottom rows can be considered as adjacent as can squares in the outside columns.

Example 7
Simplify:

$$F = A.B.\bar{C}.D + A.\bar{B}.\bar{C}.D + \bar{A}.\bar{B} + A.B.C.\bar{D} + \bar{A}.B$$

The simplified solution is:

$$F = \bar{A} + \bar{C}.D + B.C.\bar{D}.$$

Note that the term $\bar{A}.\bar{B}$ is represented by the first left-hand column of Fig. A4.11 and the term $\bar{A}.B$ by the second left-hand column. The largest group of 8 cells is encircled first, then the group of 4 cells and finally the group of two cells.

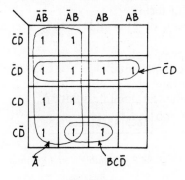

Fig. A4.11

Example 8
Simplify:

$$F = \bar{A}.\bar{B}.(\bar{C}.\bar{D} + C.\bar{D}) + \bar{B}.\bar{D}(A.\bar{C} + A.C) + B.D$$

The expression must be placed in the **sum of products** form before it can be

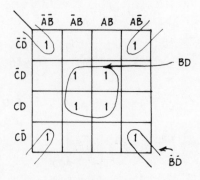

Fig. A4.12

mapped. Thus multiplying out we have:

$$F = \bar{A}.\bar{B}.\bar{C}.\bar{D} + \bar{A}.\bar{B}.C.\bar{D} + A.\bar{B}.\bar{C}.\bar{D} + A.\bar{B}.C.\bar{D} + B.D$$

This expression is mapped in Fig. A4.12. After minimisation the expression simplifies to:

$$F = \bar{B}.\bar{D} + B.D.$$

Note that the four corner squares of the map may be considered as adjacent and that the expression B.D is represented by the central four squares of the map.

Rules for 4-Variable Karnaugh Maps
1 Find any terms that will combine in one way only with another term and encircle such pair of terms.
2 Encircle any groups of four unless they are all contained in pair groupings.
3 Encircle any groups of eight.
4 Encircle any prime implicants.
5 Selecting the largest possible grouping with the least number of separate groups gives the simplest possible solution.

SYNCHRONOUS COUNTERS

IN SYNCHRONOUS COUNTERS, changes in state of the individual flip-flops are synchronised to the clock pulses and such counters are said to be **clock driven**. Synchronous counters are often designed around J-K flip-flops which are readily available in i.c. form. They often count in pure binary (up or down) but in other cases the count may be non-binary as in a B.C.D. decade counter or Gray code counter. In order to achieve the desired count, it is necessary to employ a suitable logic circuit to ensure that after the application of each clock pulse the desired state of each stage is obtained and that the logic values of the J and K inputs are set accordingly.

Modulo-4 Synchronous Up-Counter

A modulo-4 counter has four states and requires two flip-flops for its implementation. One method of design is to draw up a state table as in Fig. A5.1(a) where the first column for Q_A and Q_B represents the present state of the count and the second column gives the next state of the count after the application of a clock pulse. If the table is examined row-by-row separately for Q_A and Q_B, the transitions that have to be made for each output will be revealed as the counter goes from its present state to the next state. The values required on the J and K inputs can then be deduced.

Considering the Q_A columns of the first row it will be noted that the transition is from a '0' to a '1'. Inspection of the table in Fig. A5.1(b) reveals that the required J and K inputs are '1' and 'X' where 'X' means 'don't care' and may be a logic 1 or logic 0. The Q_A transition for the second row is from a '1' to a '0' and the required J and K inputs are 'X' and '0' respectively.

Similarly for the first row of the Q_B columns the transition is from a '0' to a '0' and the table of Fig. A5.1(b) shows that the required J and K inputs are '0' and 'X' respectively. In this manner all of the required J and K input states can be ascertained.

Inspection of the J_A and K_A inputs show that they may be at either '1' or 'X', thus it follows that $J_A = K_A = 1$.

Present state		Next state		Inputs required			
Q_B	Q_A	Q_B	Q_A	J_A	K_A	J_B	K_B
0	0	0	1	1	X	0	X
0	1	1	0	X	1	1	X
1	0	1	1	1	X	X	0
1	1	0	0	X	1	X	1

(a) State Table

Transition	J	K
0 → 1	1	X
0 → 0	0	X
1 → 1	X	0
1 → 0	X	1

X = don't care (0 or 1)

(b) J-K inputs required for transitions and non-transitions

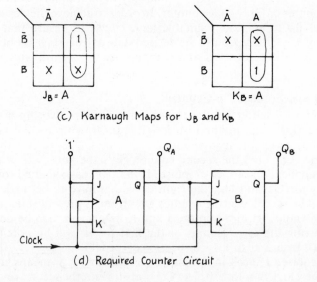

(c) Karnaugh Maps for J_B and K_B

(d) Required Counter Circuit

Fig. A5.1 Design of synchronous modulo-4 up counter.

To determine the J_B and K_B input expressions, separate Karnaugh maps are drawn as in Fig. A5.1(c) plotting the '1s' and 'Xs' for the J_B and K_B columns. After simplification it is found that $J_B = A$ and $K_B = A$. Thus the required circuit for the counter is as in Fig. A5.1(d).

Modulo-8 Synchronous Up-Counter

A modulo-8 counter has eight states and requires three flip-flops. The design of the counter may be carried out in the same manner as for the modulo-4 counter and it will be seen that adding a further flip-flop does not alter the design of the earlier stages. Thus for flip-flops A and B, $J_A = K_A = 1$ and $J_B = K_B = A$.

A state table for the counter is given in Fig. A5.2(a) which shows the required J and K input states for the three flip-flops as the respective outputs change from the present to the next state.

Karnaugh maps for the J_C and K_C inputs are given in Fig. A5.2(b). After simplification it is found that $J_C = K_C = AB$. Thus the required counter circuit may be implemented as in Fig. A5.2(c).

Present State			Next State			Inputs Required					
Q_C	Q_B	Q_A	Q_C	Q_B	Q_A	J_A	K_A	J_B	K_B	J_C	K_C
0	0	0	0	0	1	1	X	0	X	0	X
0	0	1	0	1	0	X	1	1	X	0	X
0	1	0	0	1	1	1	X	X	0	0	X
0	1	1	1	0	0	X	1	X	1	1	X
1	0	0	1	0	1	1	X	0	X	X	0
1	0	1	1	1	0	X	1	1	X	X	0
1	1	0	1	1	1	1	X	X	0	X	0
1	1	1	0	0	0	X	1	X	1	X	1

$$J_A = K_A = 1 \quad J_B = K_B = A$$

(a) State Table

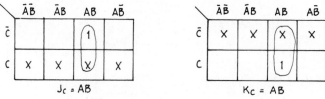

$$J_C = AB \qquad K_C = AB$$

(b) Karnaugh Maps for J_C and K_C

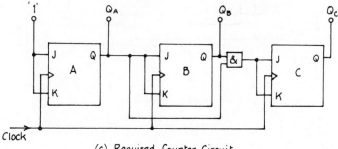

(c) Required Counter Circuit

Fig. A5.2 Design of synchronous modulo-8 up counter.

Modulo-8 Synchronous Down-Counter

A down-counter may be designed in the same manner as an up-counter and Fig. A5.3 illustrates the design for a modulo-8 down counter. The state table is given in Fig. A5.3(a) and from inspection of the required J_A and K_A inputs it will be seen that both inputs are either at logic 1 or 'don't care'. Thus

Present State			Next State			Inputs required					
Q_C	Q_B	Q_A	Q_C	Q_B	Q_A	J_A	K_A	J_B	K_B	J_C	K_C
1	1	1	1	1	0	X	1	X	0	X	0
1	1	0	1	0	1	1	X	X	1	X	0
1	0	1	1	0	0	X	1	0	X	X	0
1	0	0	0	1	1	1	X	1	X	X	1
0	1	1	0	1	0	X	1	X	0	0	X
0	1	0	0	0	1	1	X	X	1	0	X
0	0	1	0	0	0	X	1	0	X	0	X
0	0	0	1	1	1	1	X	1	X	1	X

$$J_A = K_A = 1$$

(a) State Table

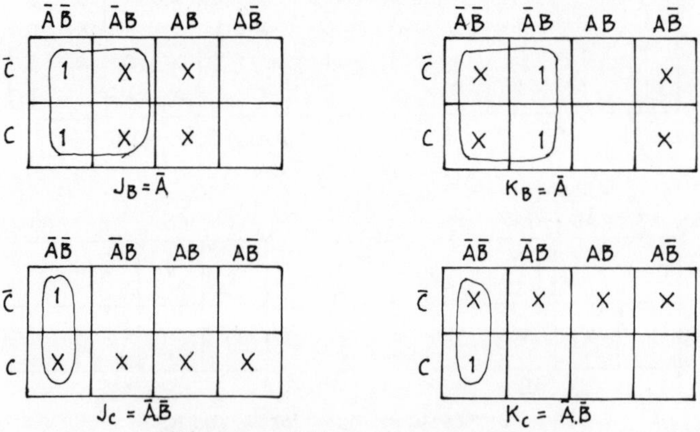

$J_B = \bar{A}$

$K_B = \bar{A}$

$J_C = \bar{A}\bar{B}$

$K_C = \bar{A}.\bar{B}$

(b) Karnaugh Maps for J_B, K_B, J_C and K_C

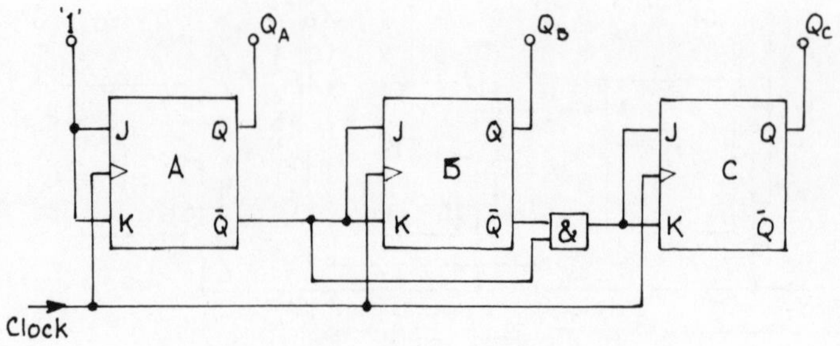

Fig. A5.3 Design of synchronous modulo-8 down counter.

it follows that $J_A = K_A = 1$ and, therefore, the first stage may be wired in the 'toggle' mode.

To determine the J_B, K_B, J_C and K_C inputs, separate Karnaugh maps are drawn as in Fig. A5.3(b). After simplification it is found that $J_B = K_B = \bar{A}$ and $J_C = K_C = \bar{A}.\bar{B}$. The counter circuit may, therefore, be implemented as in Fig. A5.3(c). Here some provision would be included to SET all Q outputs to logic 1 prior to the count commencing.

Modulo-5 and Modulo-10 Synchronous Up-Counters

The same design technique may be used when the desired count is not a power of 2. A five-state or divide-by-five counter is illustrated in Fig. A5.4.

The counter will require three flip-flops and the switching sequence may be indicated by a state diagram as in Fig. A5.4(a). This diagram shows that the circuit will cycle through the five states 0 to 1 to 2 to 3 to 4 and back to 0 . . . *etc*. Should the counter ever switch on in one of the unused states of 5, 6 or 7, the next clock pulse must cause it to join the count sequence as indicated.

Thus the unused states have been included in the state table of Fig. A5.4(b). From inspection of the table it will be seen that $K_A = 1$ and $K_C = 1$. The logic expressions for the other inputs may be arrived at by using

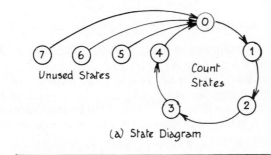

(a) State Diagram

	Present State			Next State			Inputs required					
	Q_C	Q_B	Q_A	Q_C	Q_B	Q_A	J_A	K_A	J_B	K_B	J_C	K_C
Count States	0	0	0	0	0	1	1	X	0	X	0	X
	0	0	1	0	1	0	X	1	1	X	0	X
	0	1	0	0	1	1	1	X	X	0	0	X
	0	1	1	1	0	0	X	1	X	1	1	X
Unused States	1	0	0	0	0	0	0	X	0	X	X	1
	1	0	1	0	0	0	X	1	0	X	X	1
	1	1	0	0	0	0	0	X	X	1	X	1
	1	1	1	0	0	0	X	1	X	1	X	1

(b) State Table $K_A = 1$ $K_C = 1$

Fig. A5.4 Design of synchronous modulo-5 up counter.

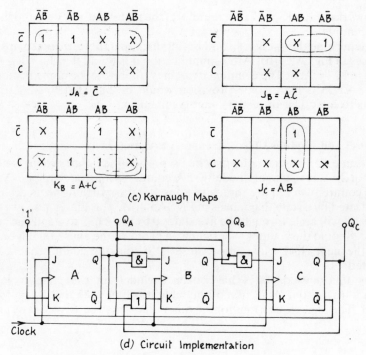

(c) Karnaugh Maps

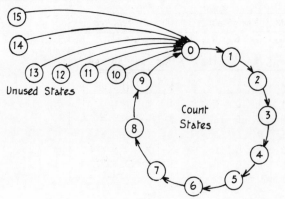

(d) Circuit Implementation

Fig. A5.4 Design of synchronous modulo-5 up counter.

Karnaugh maps and simplifying as in Fig. A5.4(c). The counter circuit may then be implemented as in Fig. A5.4(d).

A modulo-10 (decade) counter has 10 states and requires four flip-flops. Its switching sequence may be indicated by the state diagram of Fig. A5.5. Should the counter ever switch on in either of the unused states 10, 11, 12, 13, 14 or 15, the next clock pulse must cause it to join the count sequence as shown.

Fig. A5.5 State diagram for decade counter.

The state table is given in Fig. A5.6(a) which gives the required inputs for the count and unused states. From inspection it will be seen that $K_A = 1$. To deduce the expressions for the other inputs, Karnaugh maps are drawn as in

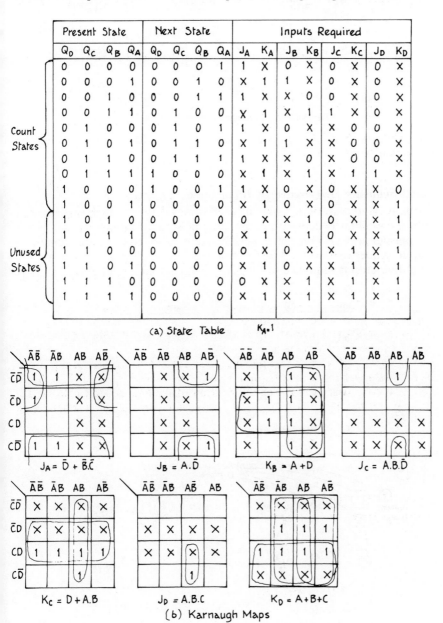

Present State				Next State				Inputs Required							
Q_D	Q_C	Q_B	Q_A	Q_D	Q_C	Q_B	Q_A	J_A	K_A	J_B	K_B	J_C	K_C	J_D	K_D
0	0	0	0	0	0	0	1	1	X	0	X	0	X	0	X
0	0	0	1	0	0	1	0	X	1	1	X	0	X	0	X
0	0	1	0	0	0	1	1	1	X	X	0	0	X	0	X
0	0	1	1	0	1	0	0	X	1	X	1	1	X	0	X
0	1	0	0	0	1	0	1	1	X	0	X	X	0	0	X
0	1	0	1	0	1	1	0	X	1	1	X	X	0	0	X
0	1	1	0	0	1	1	1	1	X	X	0	X	0	0	X
0	1	1	1	1	0	0	0	X	1	X	1	X	1	1	X
1	0	0	0	1	0	0	1	1	X	0	X	0	X	X	0
1	0	0	1	0	0	0	0	X	1	0	X	0	X	X	1
1	0	1	0	0	0	0	0	0	X	X	1	0	X	X	1
1	0	1	1	0	0	0	0	X	1	X	1	0	X	X	1
1	1	0	0	0	0	0	0	0	X	0	X	X	1	X	1
1	1	0	1	0	0	0	0	X	1	0	X	X	1	X	1
1	1	1	0	0	0	0	0	0	X	X	1	X	1	X	1
1	1	1	1	0	0	0	0	X	1	X	1	X	1	X	1

(a) State Table $\quad K_A = 1$

$J_A = \bar{D} + \bar{B}.\bar{C}$

$J_B = A.\bar{D}$

$K_B = A + D$

$J_C = A.B.\bar{D}$

$K_C = D + A.B$

$J_D = A.B.C$

$K_D = A + B + C$

(b) Karnaugh Maps

Fig. A5.6 State table and Karnaugh maps for decade counter.

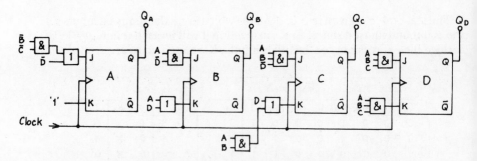

Fig. A5.7 Implementation of decade counter.

Fig. A5.6(b) which are then simplified. The counter circuit may then be implemented as in Fig. A5.7.

Count Sequence Determined by Input Code

It may be necessary to design a synchronous counter which generates an output code that is determined by the logic state of an input code.

Consider a 3-bit counter which is required to produce the repetitive output sequence of Fig. A5.8(a) when an input Z is at logic 0 or the repetitive output sequence of Fig. A5.8(b) when the input Z is at logic 1.

(a) $Z = 0$					(b) $Z = 1$			
State	C	B	A		State	C	B	A
0	0	0	0		0	0	0	0
6	1	1	0		2	0	1	0
5	1	0	1		3	0	1	1
4	1	0	0		4	1	0	0
3	0	1	1		6	1	1	0
2	0	1	0		0	0	0	0
1	0	0	1				etc	
0	0	0	0					
		etc						

Fig. A5.8 Count sequences required.

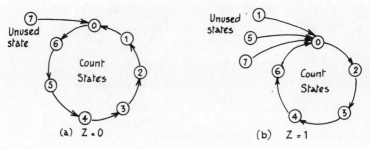

Fig. A5.9 State diagrams.

The state diagrams of Fig. A5.9 show how the counter moves from one state to the next and includes the unused states. Should the counter ever start-up in an unused state it must join the count sequence on the next clock pulse.

A state table is given in Fig. A5.10 from which the required J and K input

	Input	Present State			Next State			J-K Inputs Required					
	Z	Q_C	Q_B	Q_A	Q_C	Q_B	Q_A	J_A	K_A	J_B	K_B	J_C	K_C
Count States	0	0	0	0	1	1	0	0	X	1	X	1	X
	0	1	1	0	1	0	1	1	X	X	1	X	0
	0	1	0	1	1	0	0	X	1	0	X	X	0
	0	1	0	0	0	1	1	1	X	1	X	X	1
	0	0	1	1	0	1	0	X	1	X	0	0	X
	0	0	1	0	0	0	1	1	X	X	1	0	X
	0	0	0	1	0	0	0	X	1	0	X	0	X
Unused state	0	1	1	1	0	0	0	X	1	X	1	X	1
Count States	1	0	0	0	0	1	0	0	X	1	X	0	X
	1	0	1	0	0	1	1	1	X	X	0	0	X
	1	0	1	1	1	0	0	X	1	X	1	1	X
	1	1	0	0	1	1	0	0	X	1	X	X	0
	1	1	1	0	0	0	0	0	X	X	1	X	1
Unused States	1	0	0	1	0	0	0	X	1	0	X	0	X
	1	1	0	1	0	0	0	X	1	0	X	X	1
	1	1	1	1	0	0	0	X	1	X	1	X	1

Fig. A5.10 State table.

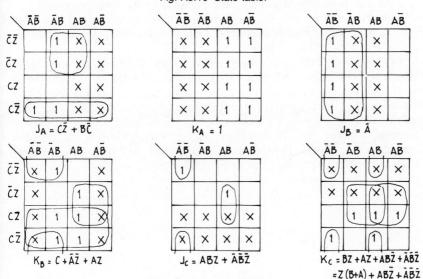

$J_A = C\bar{Z} + B\bar{C}$

$K_A = 1$

$J_B = \bar{A}$

$K_B = C + \bar{A}\bar{Z} + AZ$

$J_C = ABZ + \bar{A}\bar{B}\bar{Z}$

$K_C = BZ + AZ + AB\bar{Z} + \bar{A}\bar{B}\bar{Z}$
$= Z(B+A) + AB\bar{Z} + \bar{A}\bar{B}\bar{Z}$

Fig. A5.11 Karnaugh maps.

states for each row in the table may be determined as the count proceeds from its present state to the next state when the input Z is in the logic 0 or 1 state. Karnaugh maps are then drawn as in Fig. A5.11 which after minimisation enable the input expressions to be established.

The logic circuit may then be implemented as in Fig. A5.12.

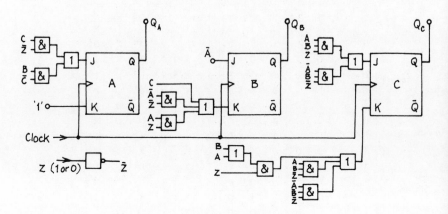

Fig. A5.12 Circuit implementation.

Gray Code Synchronous Counter

D-type and S-R flip-flops may also be used in the implementation of synchronous counters. The D-type flip-flop provides the simplest and most direct method of realising a counter, since upon clocking, the output assumes the state of the D-input.

Consider a 3-bit Gray code counter using D-type flip-flops, the state table of which is given in Fig. A5.13(a). By considering each row of the table in turn, the required state of the D inputs may be ascertained; Fig. A5.13(b) gives the state of the D input for all possible transitions as the count proceeds from the present state to the next state.

Karnaugh maps are then drawn as in Fig. A5.13(c) which after minimisation enable the D-input expressions to be established. A practical realisation of the circuit is given in Fig. A5.13(d).

Present State			Next State			D-inputs required		
Q_C	Q_B	Q_A	Q_C	Q_B	Q_A	D_A	D_B	D_C
0	0	0	0	0	1	1	0	0
0	0	1	0	1	1	1	1	0
0	1	1	0	1	0	0	1	0
0	1	0	1	1	0	0	1	1
1	1	0	1	1	1	1	1	1
1	1	1	1	0	1	1	0	1
1	0	1	1	0	0	0	0	1
1	0	1	0	0	0	0	0	0

(a) State Table

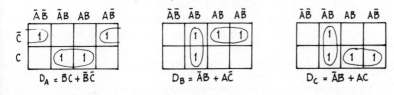

Transition	D
0 → 1	1
0 → 0	0
1 → 1	1
1 → 0	0

(b) D inputs required for transitions and non-transitions

$$D_A = BC + \bar{B}\bar{C} \qquad D_B = \bar{A}B + A\bar{C} \qquad D_C = \bar{A}B + AC$$

(c) Karnaugh Maps

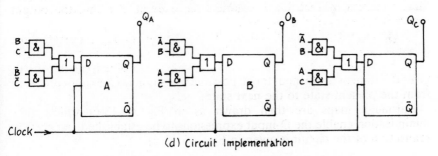

(d) Circuit Implementation

Fig. A5.13 Synchronous Gray code counter using D-type flip-flops.

B.C.D. and HEXADECIMAL CODING

Hexadecimal

HEXADECIMAL IS A hybrid numbering system using the base or radix of 16 and is a shorthand way of representing binary numbers. Hexadecimal or 'Hex' is prefered to other numbering systems such as octal in microcomputer systems due to the reduced number of digits necessary to represent any particular binary number.

Since the base is 16, 16 symbols are required:

Decimal	Hexadecimal
0	0
1	1
2	2
3	3
4	4
5	5
6	6
7	7
8	8
9	9
10	A
11	B
12	C
13	D
14	E
15	F

The column weightings are:

$$\begin{array}{ccccccc} (4096) & (256) & (16) & (1) & & (\frac{1}{16}) & (\frac{1}{256}) & (\frac{1}{4096}) \\ 16^3 & 16^2 & 16^1 & 16^0 & \cdot & 16^{-1} & 16^{-2} & 16^{-3} \end{array}$$

$\longleftarrow$ 16^3 16^2 16^1 16^0 $\cdot$ 16^{-1} 16^{-2} 16^{-3} $\longrightarrow$

Increasing in $\uparrow$ Decreasing in
powers of 16   Hexadecimal   powers of 16
                                   point

$$\begin{array}{ccc} 2 & 5 & B \end{array}$$

Thus if we write the number 25B, this means

$$
\begin{array}{ccc}
2 \times 256 = & 512 \\
+ & + \\
5 \times \;\;16 = & 80 \\
+ & + \\
11 \times \;\;\;\;1 = & \underline{11} \\
& = \;603 \text{ in decimal}
\end{array}
$$

Other examples are:

Hexadecimal	Decimal
F	15
10	16
1F	31
20	32
3F	63
40	64
FF	255
3AB	939
FFF	4095
1000	4096

Binary	Hexadecimal
1111101	7D
111111111	1FF
1010	A

A modified form of Hexadecimal coding used in Signature Analysers employs the following symbols: 0 1 2 3 4 5 6 7 8 9 A C F H P U.

Binary Coded Decimal (B.C.D.)

The binary number system is the simplest and best for logic circuits and computers, but the denary numbering system is the one that most people are familiar with. Although Hex is a shorthand version of binary it is not much help in converting binary-to-denary. To overcome these problems several binary codes have been devised to translate each denary digit into an equivalent 4-bit binary code and vice-versa. Consider the B.C.D. form of the decimal number 3459:

Thousands Decade	Hundreds Decade	Tens Decade	Units Decade
3	4	5	9
↓	↓	↓	↓
0011	0100	0101	1001

Each digit from each decade of the denary number is coded by a block of 4 binary digits. The above result may be written as:

0011   0100   0101   1001
or
0011010001011001

In the above, NATURAL binary coding is used for each decade. It will be seen that binary digits for 0 to 9 only need to be remembered since the same code is used for each decade.

Examples
Decimal-to-B.C.D.

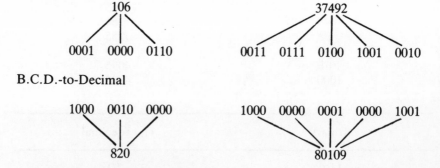

B.C.D. also simplifies the electronics of a processing system since the circuits are the same for each decade. There are several types of B.C.D. codes and the one that has been examined is known as the 8:4:2:1 code since these are the weightings for each binary digit in any decade and follows NATURAL binary weighting. Two other common B.C.D. codes are 2:4:2:1 and Excess-3 (XS3). The table below shows the comparison between the three types.

	8:4:2:1 BCD				2:4:2:1 BCD				XS3 BCD			
Weight	8	4	2	1	2	4	2	1			–	
Denary												
0	0	0	0	0	0	0	0	0	0	0	1	1
1	0	0	0	1	0	0	0	1	0	1	0	0
2	0	0	1	0	0	0	1	0	0	1	0	1
3	0	0	1	1	0	0	1	1	0	1	1	0
4	0	1	0	0	0	1	0	0	0	1	1	1
5	0	1	0	1	0	1	0	1	1	0	0	0
6	0	1	1	0	0	1	1	0	1	0	0	1
7	0	1	1	1	0	1	1	1	1	0	1	0
8	1	0	0	0	1	1	1	0	1	0	1	1
9	1	0	0	1	1	1	1	1	1	1	0	0

There is no simple weighting for the XS3 binary digits. It will be seen decimal zero is not represented by 0000 but by 0011 (Excess-3).

ASCII CHARACTER SET

THE ASCII CHARACTER set given below is for 7-bit coding, but rather than list the binary code for each character the Hex and Decimal equivalents are given.

ASCII VALUE		CHARACTER	ASCII VALUE		CHARACTER
DEC	HEX		DEC	HEX	
0	00	NUL	25	19	EM
1	01	SOH	26	1A	SUB
2	02	STX	27	1B	ESC
3	03	ETX	28	1C	FS
4	04	EOT	29	1D	CS
5	05	ENQ	30	1E	RS
6	06	ACK	31	1F	US
7	07	BEL	32	20	Space
8	08	BS	33	21	!
9	09	HT	34	22	"
10	0A	NL	35	23	#(US) £(UK)
11	0B	VT	36	24	$
12	0C	FF	37	25	%
13	0D	RT	38	26	&
14	0E	SO	39	27	'
15	0F	SI	40	28	(
16	10	DLE	41	29	)
17	11	DC1	42	2A	*
18	12	DC2	43	2B	+
19	13	DC3	44	2C	,
20	14	DC4	45	2D	−
21	15	NAK	46	2E	.
22	16	SYN	47	2F	/
23	17	ETB	48	30	0
24	18	CAN	49	31	1

ASCII VALUE		CHARACTER	ASCII VALUE		CHARACTER
DEC	HEX		DEC	HEX	
50	32	2	89	59	Y
51	33	3	90	5A	Z
52	34	4	91	5B	[
53	35	5	92	5C	\
54	36	6	93	5D	]
55	37	7	94	5E	^
56	38	8	95	5F	—
57	39	9	96	60	´
58	3A	:	97	61	a
59	3B	;	98	62	b
60	3C	‹	99	63	c
61	3D	=	100	64	d
62	3E	›	101	65	e
63	3F	?	102	66	f
64	40	@	103	67	g
65	41	A	104	68	h
66	42	B	105	69	i
67	43	C	106	6A	j
68	44	D	107	6B	k
69	45	E	108	6C	l
70	46	F	109	6D	m
71	47	G	110	6E	n
72	48	H	111	6F	o
73	49	I	112	70	p
74	4A	J	113	71	q
75	4B	K	114	72	r
76	4C	L	115	73	s
77	4D	M	116	74	t
78	4E	N	117	75	u
79	4F	O	118	76	v
80	50	P	119	77	w
81	51	Q	120	78	x
82	52	R	121	79	y
83	53	S	122	7A	z
84	54	T	123	7B	{
85	55	U	124	7C		
86	56	V	125	7D	}
87	57	W	126	7E	~
88	58	X	127	7F	△

(0–31) are control characters

INDEX